The Watermills of Britain

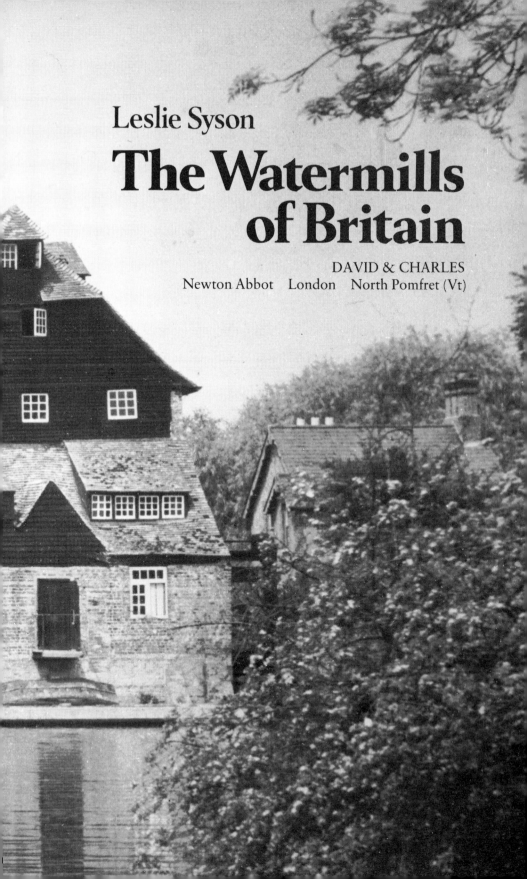

Leslie Syson

The Watermills
of Britain

DAVID & CHARLES
Newton Abbot   London   North Pomfret (Vt)

British Library Cataloguing in Publication Data

Syson, Leslie
    The watermills of Britain.
    1. Watermills – Great Britain
    I. Title
    621.2'1   TJ859

ISBN 0–7153–7824–4

Photoset, printed and bound in Great Britain by
Redwood Burn Limited Trowbridge & Esher
for David & Charles (Publishers) Limited
Brunel House Newton Abbot Devon

Published in the United States of America
by David & Charles Inc
North Pomfret Vermont 05053 USA

CONTENTS

6   *Contents*

INTRODUCTION

Whatever may be generally known of watermills, many people have used, or at least heard, the phrase 'as calm [or as flat] as a millpond'. Not all mills need a millpond but where one exists, there is that combination which modern industry can seldom offer – peace and power. The millpond is an attractive, peaceful scene where one can stand and gaze as if into a mirror, seeing anything the imagination cares to conjure up. Nature provides a frame for that mirror, gradually changing it through the seasons of the year and never repeating the scene at another mill. Often there will be rushes, waving gently as the water almost imperceptibly passes by and if there is sufficient breeze, providing musical accompaniment too. There may even be water-lilies or bulrushes in the water and snowdrops or daffodils on the bank to add colour, according to the time of year. Then, if the observer can match the stillness of the water, the graceful movements of the kingfisher or moorhen offer their reward.

This scene is, however, not just one of tranquillity. The millpond is also a power-house, a store of energy for the mill – not pouring out toxic fumes and billowing clouds of smoke or clanging noisily like some giant factory, but calmly waiting its turn to drive the wheel. On the other side of the mill, this peaceful store of energy is transformed. It leaves the wheel bouncing and bubbling over with energy! The quietness is changed for the rush and roar of water which seems to have only one object in mind – to be on the way to the next mill. How can the water authorities of today claim such large amounts for 'the right to abstract water' when it is still there to be used again?

Novelists, poets, painters and photographers have all obtained inspiration from watermills. Tennyson must have been well acquainted with the mill scene when he wrote 'The Miller's Daughter', and perhaps he realised the power of the brook when he wrote:

> For men may come, and men may go,
> But I go on for ever.

The nineteenth-century poet Sarah Doudney saw in the mill not only a picturesque scene but also a lesson to be learnt:

> Listen to the watermill;
> Through the livelong day,
> How the clicking of its wheel
> Wears the hours away!
> Languidly the autumn wind
> Stirs the forest leaves.
> From the field the reapers sing,
> Binding up their sheaves;
> And a proverb haunts my mind
> As a spell is cast:
> 'The mill cannot grind
> With the water that is past'.
>
> from 'The Lesson of the Watermill'

Chaucer gives a clear description of the miller of Trumpington in *The Canterbury Tales*, a master hand at stealing grain, typical, unfortunately, of the times in which he lived. More recently, the mill at Gainsborough in Lincolnshire has provided George Eliot with a setting for *The Mill on the Floss*, though nothing remains of the site Dorlcote Mill is believed to have occupied. Other novels have been written around the Abbey mills at Wool in Dorset and at Tewkesbury; the latter is now a pleasant restaurant.

The attraction of the watermill to artists is widespread but John Constable is no doubt the best known for his watercolours of his father's mill at Flatford and the nearby Dedham Mill. But though the prints and photographs of colourful mill scenes that frequently appear on greetings cards and calendars give pleasure, nothing can equal the experience of a personal visit if this is possible.

However, not every aspect of a mill is as attractive in that artistic sense. From the early days of the watermill's invention – probably 2,500 years ago – the history of its development contains numerous accounts of arguments and legal wrangles. The new device offered the prospect of relieving the maidservants of their irksome task of grinding corn for the daily bread, but in some cases it was received with doubt and suspicion and in others with claims of redundancy, even in those far-off days. Eventually, the mill became the hub of activity in many a community where a natural supply of water power existed. It was a meeting place for all involved in growing grain and baking bread.

The use of the watermill is in no way limited to grinding corn. Its applications have been many and varied, and even the materials to be ground have ranged from snuff to gunpowder. Water-powered mills ground flint for the pottery-making industry; fulling mills were an essential part of the woollen trade; the steel industry of Sheffield became dependent upon the waterwheel; Richard Arkwright built large cotton mills in Lancashire and Derbyshire – and so the development went on. By the time the Industrial Revolution had made its impact the country was probably as dependent on the waterwheel as it is now on electricity. The history of the manufacture of some of our well-known products of today, like Colman's mustard and Ferodo brake linings, goes back to a waterwheel beginning.

The waterwheel reached its peak of performance in the nineteenth century, but the pace of technological development was increasing and new sources of energy soon took over. The water turbine, the closest descendant of the waterwheel, proved more efficient, but it is far more complex in design and construction with its carefully shaped blades, fully enclosed chambers and various forms of inflow and pressures. The development of this and of power from steam, electricity and the petrol engine all combined to make the waterwheel redundant. The simplicity of its action, its ease of maintenance and its economy of operation, using a natural source of power, were forgotten, and our growing greed for energy from expendable fuels began.

Now the watermill is in retirement. Gradually, many fell into decay, being of no further use, but in recent years their value and attractiveness have been more fully realised. Some are preserved, fortunately, as fully operational mills and others as museums of various kinds, while some have been converted, with varying degrees of honesty, into dwellings for those who seek quiet, colourful surroundings. It is interesting that Field Marshal Lord Montgomery, after fighting the noisy battles of the dusty North African desert in World War II, acquired a quiet, peaceful mill on the River Wey in Hampshire.

Many mill sites in Britain have been in use since the time of the Domesday survey – for almost a thousand years! It is, therefore, only right that the end of such a long period of operation, providing such essential services to the nation, should be suitably recognised and marked. Future generations will not grow up, as so many have in the past, with a mill as an accepted part of their lives; however, it is pleasing that there are mills available now for visitors to see. One hopes that such people are not just mesmerised by the rhythm and revolutions of the wheels and stones, but that they do appreciate the contribution the watermill has made to the development of our present society.

Hence, this book is an attempt to make known some of the mills and some of the interesting details that are to be found. No doubt readers may feel that some mills have been omitted whilst others have been given too much attention. Certainly, there are others to be found, and it is hoped that the reader finds pleasure in seeking them. Few mills are open all the year round; more commonly they can be seen during summer months or on special 'open days'. Some of the privately owned mills are not open to the public at all. Where possible this information has been given, but in all cases it would be advisable to check the opening times to avoid disappointment and wasted journeys.

Part One

The History of The Watermill

IN THE BEGINNING

Necessity is the parent of invention and little could be more necessary than food. Although the power a waterwheel can produce has been harnessed for a wide variety of purposes, it is in the preparation of food that we find much of the early history that led to the development of the waterwheel.

When early man, many thousands of years ago, began to live a less nomadic life, more attention was given to growing cereals and therefore to their processing. The book of Numbers records: 'And the manna was a coriander seed . . . and the people went about and gathered it and ground it in mills or beat it in a mortar.' Millet was used for making a kind of bread from a very early date but Ovid (43 BC–AD 17) wrote of herbs as man's first food, followed by nuts, particularly the acorn. Flour from acorns is very bitter but by passing boiling water several times through the acorns, much of the bitterness can be removed. Writing a little later, Pliny, in his *Historica Naturalis*, records the use of thirteen varieties of nuts – including acorns and beech nuts – claiming that acorns constituted the wealth of many nations. Chestnuts were dried and ground into flour, producing an easily digestible food.

The earliest implement for making meal was the hammer stone, probably used on any suitably hollow surface in nearby rocks. It would be held in a clenched fist and its wide, flat, bottom surface used to pound the nuts or grain. Examples have been found in a number of places, particularly in Texas and also in Britain, in Kent's Cavern, Torquay. Discoveries have been made in other areas of *bullán* stones, large boulders with several hollow depressions made in the surface, some containing loose stones almost filling the depressions; they were used in a mortar and pestle action. But it was the saddle stone that made a significant step forward towards grinding rather than crushing. The concave upper surface resembled the seat of a saddle on which was worked, in a backward and forward rather than a rolling movement, a muller stone. This was tapered at each end to form a suitable grip for each hand and was operated by a kneeling woman; it required the full force of arms and body, but provided more effective action than mere hammering.

The saddle stone was common in Egyptian civilisation and was used by the Romans from the time when Rome was founded in 753 BC. In various forms, it was probably used in many parts of the world. Mexican examples, often standing on legs carved in the stone, were used for grinding maize to make tortillas – thin flat cakes eaten hot. In India, they were used for grinding turmeric for making curry.

QUERNS

The progression to a quern, using a revolving stone instead of the backward and forward motion, was an important stage in the history of milling. The earliest reference is probably that made by Cato (232–147 BC) in his account of farming equipment which includes a revolving mill driven by an ass. Hand querns were no doubt common by this time and remained in use for many centuries.

The revolt of tenants at St Alban's Abbey, Cirencester in 1381 was caused by the use of hand querns against the wishes of the abbot. More of this later. Even in this century the use of hand querns, operated by two women, has been noted in the Middle East. Biblical references to milling do not make it clear what type of stone was used. However, the writer of the book of Exodus refers to 'the first born of the maid servant that is behind the mill', whereas St Matthew writes that '*two* women [my italics] shall be grinding at the mill'. Since most saddlestones would be operated by one person and the hand quern, more easily by two, these references may indicate the latter's period of development.

The quern consisted of two stones. The upper stone was turned by a vertical wooden handle that fitted into a hole near the stone's edge; in the centre would be a larger hole, probably funnel-shaped, through which the grain was fed. As already indicated, the quern would often be operated by two women, one to feed in the grain and one to turn the stone. It was acknowledged to be a task for women, and frequently both might assist in providing the turning power. Early forms of bed or lower stones were dome-shaped with the intention that ground flour would be provided with a natural fall to the rim of the stone. Gradually the grinding faces of the stones became flatter until only a slight convexity remained. There is little doubt that this was linked with the development of a system of grooves which were cut into the meeting surfaces of the stones, resulting in a grinding rather than a crushing action. An example of furrowing in five sections, on a quern stone 20in in diameter, has been found on a Roman site in Britain. More sophisticated methods were to follow but the principle was already established in preparation for the watermill.

Another principle to be developed at about the same time was that of attaching a wooden or iron bridge across the centre of the upper stone to transfer its weight on to a spindle fixed in the middle of the lower stone. This basic idea was to be used for thousands of years in water-powered corn mills. During early Christendom in Rome, querns were in quite common use and one of their purposes was frequently for crushing olives. Adjustment of the gap between the stones, made possible by adopting the bridging principle, was necessary so that the flesh of the fruit could be crushed without breaking the stones. Virgil (70–19 BC) describes the quern as an implement found in peasants' cottages of his time, and it is likely that such milling devices would accompany Roman armies on expeditions, probably including those to Britain. At one time, a mill was provided for every ten men.

The use of hand querns continued for a considerable period, but at the same time, the use of animal power also developed – the ass, camel, horse or ox being harnessed to the upper stone to cause it to revolve. This method of providing power, at least for irrigation, has continued right into the twentieth century. I remember seeing in Malta, in the 1940s, blindfolded donkeys tramping around in 20ft diameter circles to draw water from wells.

The stones of animal mills, used in many of the Mediterranean countries, were much larger than those used for hand querns. Millstones must have been well-known possessions in New Testament times since Christ refers to them to illustrate the treatment of an offender: '. . .it were better for him that a millstone were hanged about his neck, and that he were drowned in the depth of the sea'. Several translations clearly suggest that this refers to the ass mill, which adds more weight to the saying!

THE APPEARANCE OF THE WATERWHEEL

REASONS FOR DELAY

The waterwheel did not make a rapid and sweeping entrance into milling. Several factors causing the delay have already been suggested – hand querns may have been a common piece of domestic equipment, and animal power was available for larger-scale production – and in addition, slave labour was plentiful. Why be concerned? There were influential people who believed that if slaves and other workers were to be relieved of much of their labour, this might lead to idleness and unrest. Emperor Vespasian, who reigned AD 69–79, was among those opposed to the introduction of water power, fearing the effects of the widespread unemployment that might result. There was no feeling that laborious, repetitive work needed to be transferred from men or animals to some other form of power.

There were other factors too. Mediterranean rivers were not a great inspiration to anyone seeking a natural power source since few rivers could provide sufficient water all the year round to turn a waterwheel economically. Furthermore, it was the belief of many people of that time that some kind of supernatural power was hidden in the forces of nature and that to interfere with them would be blasphemous.

On the other hand, the production of grain was increasing, as was the demand for it. Caius Gracchus, in 122 BC, began a monthly distribution of grain to the Roman poor at half the market price; during the reign of Julius Caesar, 320,000 people benefitted from the scheme, though the number fluctuated from time to time. Much of this grain was produced by animal power and by criminals required to grind as a punishment – a method of treating prisoners which, incidentally, was used in this country until the nineteenth century when Elizabeth Fry objected to the excessive amount of treadmilling some were expected to do.

An indication of the amount of milling done by animal power can be gained from the incident when Caligula, Emperor of Rome from AD 37 until his assassination in AD 41, confiscated all horses owned by civilians in preparation for a large-scale military operation. The immediate result of the order was a shortage of flour.

THE GREEK MILL

The Greeks had a great respect for water. An indication of this is given by Thales of Miletus (c 640–546 BC) who expressed the belief that the *arché* or prime element of all things was water. It is also known that Hero of Alexandria, in writing *The Pneumatica* in about 150 BC, had some knowledge of various applications of water power such as water organs. One of the earliest direct references to a watermill is that made by the Greek geographer Strabo (c 66 BC–AD 24). He gives a detailed description of the ancient world in seventeen books and refers, in the twelfth, to a hydraulic machine which belonged to Mithridates – King of Pontus in the mountainous region of Paryadres near the Black Sea – and was discovered after his defeat by the Romans in 65 BC.

Strabo's account does not indicate a new invention but does suggest something of importance. But it may have been Antipater of Thessalonica – though Shemuel Avitsur suggests the earlier Antipater of Sidon – who not only recorded the dawn of the waterwheel but also foresaw its possible impact in his descriptive poetry, written in about 85 BC. Dr Tennant translated it:

> Ye maids who toiled so faithful at the mill,
> Now cease your work, and from those toils be still:
> Sleep now till dawn, and let the birds with glee
> Sing to the ruddy morn on bush and tree;
> For what your hands performed so long and true
> Ceres has charged the water nymphs to do.

The writer was most probably referring to a very simple type that has become known as the Greek mill, consisting of a vertical shaft on which a horizontal wheel was mounted. Since no gearing was involved it was comparatively straightforward to construct and could be made from local materials, by local craftsmen, to satisfy local needs. However, a reasonable force of water would be required: a head of at least 4ft. The water was directed along a trough on to the blades or vanes mortised into the hub. The shaft passed through the lower stone and was then wedged into a hole in the upper stone, causing it to revolve with the wheel.

News of such inventions travelled at a very steady pace in those days, of course. To what areas, and in what time, it is difficult to state with accuracy; no doubt traders along the Mediterranean routes carried ideas with them, as would travellers into Europe. A similar type of waterwheel is known to have existed in China; it was used for operating bellows for a furnace at an ironworks in AD 1313 and is believed to have developed from the horizontal wheels used for over a thousand years. Whether there was any connection with the invention of the Greek mill is a matter of conjecture.

Horizontal wheels have existed in many parts of the world, playing as important a role in preparing food as the plough has in growing it. Whatever routes it took around the world, the principle became very widely used in Norway during the eighteenth and nineteenth centuries. This more recent version of the horizontal wheel has thus become known as the Norse mill; it has been used throughout the Islands of Orkney and Shetland, the Faeroes, the Western Isles and the north of Scotland. Introduction of this type of mill to such remote areas is believed by Kenneth Williamson to have occurred no earlier than the eighteenth century. More details are given in later chapters.

VITRUVIAN WHEELS

The development of the waterwheel towards a more sophisticated piece of engineering is recorded by Marcus Vitruvius. His knowledge of Greek and Roman architecture, his experience as an 'engineer' – serving under Julius Caesar in Africa as an inspector of military engines – and his ability as a writer combined to provide a very detailed account of the Roman mill.

In his work *De Architectura*, probably written between 20 and 13 BC, he describes how large-diameter wheels with horizontal shafts were being used as 'engines for raising water' in Spain and other countries. The force of water striking the paddles of the wheel caused it to revolve. At the same time, buckets attached to the rim filled with water which was emptied into irrigation troughs on reaching the top of the wheel. The use of wheels with horizontal shafts involved the introduction of gearing which Vitruvius describes:

> . . . on one end of the axis C is a toothed tympanum or drum B, with a pin for bolting it to the axis. This tympanum is set perpendicularly on edge, and is turned equally with the waterwheel. Connected with this tympanum is a larger one D, toothed and placed horizontally, and containing an axis E at the top of which is an iron mortise F, which is inserted in the millstone marked G. Thus the teeth of the tympanum B which is bolted on to the axis C impel the teeth of the horizontal tympanum D and effect the rotation of the mill, the suspended hopper above supplying the grain to the stones and the rotation of the latter ejecting the flour.

Despite the considerably greater efficiency of the vertical wheel, three or four centuries elapsed before it became widely used. Slave and animal labour could be obtained easily and of course the Vitruvian-

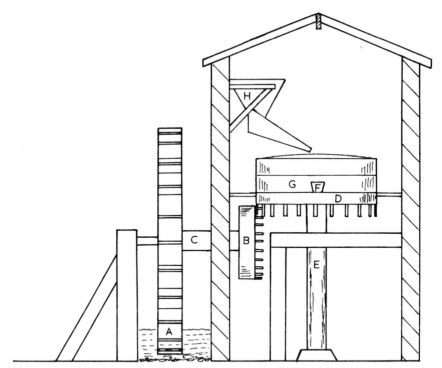

Fig 1　Diagrammatic representation of the mill described by Vitruvius

type mill was more complex to construct. Christian influence led to the abolition of slavery in the fourth century, after which there are more references to the new-style mill. There was the mill at Venafro, near Naples, with a wheel 7ft in diameter, which could grind 400lb of corn an hour, forty times more than animal power might have produced. Excavations in the Athenian Agora in 1933 revealed the remains of a Roman watermill, sufficient to establish that it had an overshot wheel approximately 10ft 6in in diameter and 1ft 6in wide, driving stones about 2ft 6in in diameter. It is believed to have been built about AD 460 and to have worked until 122 years later when it was probably destroyed in the Slav invasion.

WATER POWER IN BRITAIN

THE ROMAN ERA

Evidence to establish the earliest use of water power in Britain is difficult to find. The Roman armies would have needed considerable amounts of food. The provision of hand querns has already been mentioned, but they may also have had the benefit of the expertise of military engineers such as Vitruvius. It must be remembered, however, that the attitude of the times was still very much towards slave labour where available; this may explain why most evidence of Roman use of water power has been found along Hadrian's Wall where Roman forces were likely to be strong and slave labour low. Excavations in 1907 revealed ruins of a building believed to be a watermill, with its head and tail race traceable, on Haltwhistle Burn, a tributary of the South Tyne. This probably served the nearby fort and civil settlement at Great Chesters (*Aesca*). Then at Chesters (*Cilvrnvm*) more excavations have revealed part of a building that has been used as a mill, with head and tail race, on the North Tyne. On the River Irthing, which flows into the River Eden, remains of a watermill have been found near the point where it crosses the wall at Willowford, again probably to supply a nearby fort at Birdaswald (*Camboglanna*).

For the period following the departure of the Romans in AD 410, information about the use of water power in Britain is scanty. Christian influence was spreading and its objection to slavery began to have some effect. St Augustine's arrival in AD 597 was well received by Aethelbert of Kent and the Church grew steadily, but a settled state did not prevail in the country for several centuries. It is generally accepted that the earliest reference to a watermill was made in a charter dated AD 762, granting the use of a mill 'in the district called Cert, situated at the east of the city of Dover, which appertains to the monastery of the blessed apostles Peter and Paul'.

SAXON MILLS

Saxon craftsmanship was developing and some of their architecture, particularly the ecclesiastical, remains to testify to this. Reconstructions of Saxon waterwheels are to be seen in the Science Museum in South Kensington, London, and more evidence to demonstrate Saxon ability has come to light in recent years. A unique opportunity occurred in Tamworth, in 1971, with the demolition of houses in Bolebridge Street. At a point just above the confluence of the River Anker with the River Tame, excavations revealed a framework of pegged planks forming part of a mill. Erosion appeared to have damaged the leat so much that the site was abandoned. But a second mill site was discovered, the remains showing quite an elaborate oak structure frequently using the mortise and tenon, with a small second mortise in the extra long tenon which projects through the main mortise. A wedge through the second mortise then held the joint together. The evidence suggests that water was stored in a millpool, from which it passed through a double sluice into two channels – one to the wheel and one to bypass it. Radiocarbon dating tests on samples taken from the mill leats and pool areas place the most probable date as within the eighth century. The type of wheel was probably horizontal. Excavations in Old Windsor during the 1950s unearthed a ninth-century mill which is believed to have had a vertical wheel.

References to mills appear frequently in Saxon charters and codes of law during the tenth century. Winchester was the financial head-quarters for the Saxons so it is not surprising that several mills are mentioned as being situated there in 983 during the reign of King Ethelred II.

THE DOMESDAY BOOK

The Normans, in looking for means of raising taxes, expected a worthwhile income from existing mills and therefore listed them in the Domesday survey. The exact number of watermills working at that time is difficult to determine. Only one word is used to describe a mill and it is possible that in some cases it could refer to an animal mill or to a hand mill. It is not likely to have referred to a building, but rather to the mill inside – a pair of stones. If a building contained two or three pairs of stones, as was certainly the case in later years, then the number of sites is very much affected. There may also have been what might be termed 'clerical errors'. No mill, for example, is listed for Ashby by Partney in Leicestershire, but another folio refers to a dispute over a mill there! Another complication is that some mills were shared between two, three or even more settlements and may, therefore, be included more than once in the total figures. Finally, the whole of the country was not covered by the survey. No mention is made of Northumbria and Durham, nor are any mills listed for Lancashire and Cumbria — areas which, later at least, showed a prolific supply of suitable sites for watermills. Cornwall is credited with only six mills which is surprisingly low for its ample supply of suitable streams.

We can be fairly certain that the term used did not refer to windmills. The earliest known references were made in 1185 to one at Weedley in East Yorkshire and to another in Suffolk in 1191. So the number of Domesday mills seems to be about 5,624, and it is believed that all but a hundred or so of these sites can be accounted for. On average, each mill would serve about fifty households. There is, therefore, evidence of the mill being firmly established as an important part of the country's economy. It was a meeting point within a community. The miller was developing the craft of controlling his water supply, the skill in using his millstones and the knowledge of materials needed to produce his simple machinery. Those who grew the corn, those who baked with the flour and those who ate the bread, all had some contact with the miller. Who else remained?

The annual value placed on a mill varied from 3d to £42 9s 8d for the seven at Battersea. Payment to the lord of the manor was sometimes made in silver or other valuables — even eels, which were a common by-product of a watermill. Eels were usually delivered on sticks, twenty-five eels, for example, on a stick. Some mills are described as 'winter mills'; these were usually of low value, probably indicating that the water supply dried up in summer. For one settlement, the entry reads: 'Here is a mill rendering nothing except a living for him who keeps it.'

Quarries are also mentioned in the Domesday survey. At Watone in Nottinghamshire, a 'molaria' where millstones were dug yielded four silver marks per annum and one at Bigeneyre in Sussex yielded 4s. Quernsmoor, near Lancaster, and Quorn, between Loughborough and Leicester, obviously provided early hand mills.

What type of watermill was used during this period is not clear. Some may have been the simple Norse type with no gearing, but many sites still in existence that can be traced back to the Domesday survey have sufficient head of water to suggest strongly that the Roman vertical type of wheel would have been more likely.

OH, PEACEFUL ENGLAND?

An interesting reference to watermills was made in 1180 by William Fitzstephen in his biography, *Vita Sancti Thomae*, of Thomas à Becket for whom he was personal secretary. He describes the delightful plain of meadowland, north of London, interspersed with flowing streams, 'on which stand mills, whose clack is very pleasing to the ear'. What a change – a pleasant sound! Now we think of noise abatement and of wearing earmuffs.

The watermill continued to develop steadily as an important landmark in many communities for two or three centuries. To landowners fortunate enough to have a suitable stream or river flowing through their land – and many had – it was a valuable source of income. Many mills of this period, therefore, were manorial mills, serving the tenants, servants and the family of the lord of the manor. Details of such mills appear in numerous charters granting mill rights to new landowners. But it was a period not without its problems. Who owned the water? Who should control its use? Whose corn should be ground at the mill and on what terms?

The Romans had experienced difficulties in avoiding obstructions on their navigable streams and had prohibited by law the building of mill dams. English laws began to follow a similar pattern. The first law appears in the Black Book of the Admiralty of 1360, probably originally made in 1216. The Lord High Admiral was empowered to survey any mill and to order its removal should it be found to obstruct a stream or harbour. Any mill set up on salt water which caused sand, stones or earth to build up an obstruction was in danger of being pulled down by the sheriff on the instructions of the Lord High Admiral. It would be interesting to know how often this power was put into effect. Some incidents are recorded. In 1268, for example, the Abbot of St Peter's had a mill built on the Severn at Shrewsbury impeding navigation. Strong objections were made, but agreement was reached without recourse to legal action: the mill was removed!

BUILDING OF WEIRS

Building a weir, so that water could be drawn off from a main stream to flow through a mill, was a means of overcoming obstruction problems. One of the earliest recorded was built on the Thames in 1306, the first of twenty-three to be built within sixty-two miles. Some problems may have been solved, but, as often happens, others were created. An Act of Parliament in 1352 allowed for weirs and causeways to be surveyed so that if any had been raised, they had to be amended to the original level. Causeways, or causeys as they were sometimes called, set up after the time of Edward I could be destroyed forthwith. Obviously, the greed of one mill was robbing the continuous working of another downstream. The making of hiddles or barriers in a river or stream to catch fish was another increasing practice which caused more and more problems and so had to be curbed. With Wednesdays and Fridays as meatless days, and the strength of monastic influence, there was a sizeable demand for fish. An indication of the method of trapping fish is to be seen in the Luttrell Psalter of about 1338 which also shows an overshot wheel, clearly well established by that time.

Another Act, in 1399, confirmed that of 1352, but in 1422 the control of milling matters was considered no longer appropriate for the Lord High Admiral. It was handed over to the Commissioner of Sewers!

MONASTIC MILLS

In addition to the many mills owned by lords of the manor, many were owned by another large group of landowners – the monastic orders. The most important were the Benedictine, Cluniac and Cistercian orders, but the number grew to a peak of probably over 800 establishments in the fourteenth century, many with a large number not only of monks but also of hired servants and retainers, making quite sizeable communities to be fed and housed. Consequently, where a site was available, a watermill was a valuable asset. There was not only wheat to be ground for baking bread, but also barley for brewing the abbey beer: from some abbey records, it is obvious that the latter was an important and frequent task. The barley was soaked in water in the malthouse, which encouraged it to shoot; it then had to be dried in a kiln before being ground at the mill. A kiln can be found to have existed at many mills, and the ruins of Waverley Abbey and Fountains Abbey provide examples.

At many monastic sites it was the custom that all the activities of the monks should be within the confines of the abbey boundaries as far as possible. Indeed St Benedict made it a clear rule that 'all things necessary, such as water, a mill and a garden and all the various crafts should be situated so that there is no need for the monks to go abroad'. At some sites, as at Kirkstall for example, an artificial channel was constructed to divert water from a pond outside the boundary wall to the mill inside.

A practical, functional approach was the main consideration in the building and working of a monastic mill. Adornment and display of craftsmanship in wood and stone were primarily reserved for the place of worship. Consequently the craftsmen among the monks devoted their skills to building mills with solid structures which were to last many years – unless, of course, there was a fire, as in the case of Fountains Abbey in 1147 only twelve years after building began. In that instance the fire was caused by partisans of the Archbishop of York, but in other cases a thatched roof, as is shown on the mill in the

Luttrell Psalter, may have increased the risk of fire. The mill at Fountains Abbey was built over a leat from the River Skell and is believed to have had two waterwheels. At Reading, the abbey mill was built on Holy Brook, a leat dug by the monks from the River Kennet. The Benedictine monks at St Alban's had several mills. There had been three at the time of the Domesday survey, but a map of 1634 shows only two. These were on the River Ver, probably using a Roman causeway as a mill dam.

The same order of monks used a leat taken from the Thames at Abingdon. Again it was a good choice of site for water power, and it appears that the Saxons should take the credit since the first abbey there was founded by Hean, a Saxon nobleman, in AD 675. Two mills are mentioned as 'within the court' in the Domesday survey. By 1556 there were three mills and a fulling mill, and though the latter was in ruins, the manufacture of woollen cloth had been an important occupation. A mill still exists on the site – though in disuse – having two wheels driving seven pairs of stones.

The supply of water to the mill at Rievaulx Abbey in Yorkshire came from the River Rye but the exact course of the leat is in some doubt. The present mill, which is supplied by water from three ponds, originally worked three pairs of stones and is still in working order. Also in Yorkshire, Easby Abbey was granted a mill soon after its foundation in 1152. A leat from the River Swale drove the wheel at the corn mill for centuries but this finally gave way to a turbine during this century to provide electricity for the village of Easby.

Durham has had a good source of water power since the tenth century, with a mill on each side of the weir above which Durham Cathedral stands. Westminster Abbey drew the power for its watermill from the River Tyburn which flowed along its boundary. Much of its history is obscure but there are records of some of its activities from the fourteenth to the sixteenth century. While it was being rebuilt in 1381, the monks arranged for the use of the mill at Wandsworth.

There are at least thirty monastic sites in the country where buildings, ruins or records show that a watermill existed. But there are many other mills that have been, at some time in their history, owned monastically, often in situations where the monastery itself was not built on a water supply. Hambleden Mill on the River Thames is one example; it is recorded in the Domesday survey and around 1235 was granted to Keynsham Abbey, Somerset. Another example is the mill at Belton in Leicestershire, once owned by the monks of Grace Dieu. Where an abbey did not possess a mill, it was general for the neighbouring lord of the manor to allow the abbey corn to be ground 'toll and hopper free' at his mill. Stanlawe Abbey in Cheshire, for example, had that kind of arrangement. There were other situations where monasteries went to considerable lengths to be self-sufficient. At Syon House, originally established as a nunnery in 1415, a lengthy channel was cut to bring water from the River Crane to the mill. It has since been known as the Duke of Northumberland's river, the Duke having been granted ownership by James I.

OPPOSITION TO QUERNS

A charter granted in about 1150 is one of the earliest documents referring to milling. Cecilia de Rumelia, lady of the manor of Silsden, Yorkshire, endowed the monks of Embsay Priory, later transferred to Bolton, with the mill of Silsden. The more interesting point about the document is that it prohibited the building of any other mill 'by any other man'. Furthermore, it prohibited the local people from possessing hand mills and still more, compelled them to take their corn to Silsden Mill to be ground. Failure to comply with this regulation was likely to lead to confiscation of the sack of corn and the horse carrying it, as well as a penalty.

Manorial landlords contributed to the battle against hand querns in order to make sure of a full amount of work for their mills. Querns were obtained by fair means or foul and then destroyed by breaking the upper stone. In some cases, a quern may well have been a treasured possession, used and handed down by several generations. The ill-feeling can be imagined and this was to grow at times into uncontrollable dimensions. The outstanding example is to be found in the history of St Alban's Abbey, Cirencester, going back to 1274 when the abbot, as lord of the manor, began to demand hand mills from local people. For some years the situation was tolerated but then the abbot had the homes searched and found about eighty querns in use. These were confiscated and used to pave a floor at the abbey. There they remained as a reminder of the abbot's authority for a further fifty years. Then in the Peasants' Revolt of 1381, the local people could control their anger no longer; they broke into the abbey and tore up the floor, breaking the stones into pieces. The abbot struck back, collecting more querns; the townspeople fought again, taking the matter to Cirencester Assizes, but the abbot finally triumphed.

Similar events took place at Vale Royal Abbey in Cheshire where the abbot possessed milling rights for nearby Dernhall, granted in 1299. A rebellion in 1329 ended with offending objectors being led with straw halters round their necks in submission to the milling rights of the abbey. The Prior of Dunstable also faced similar problems in 1229. He finally appealed to the Bishop of Lincoln who helped to quell the riot.

Less drastic methods were used at some sites, as in Therfield in 1323, when those villeins found to have obtained hand mills were fined 40d each 'because they grind their own corn and other folks' to the prejudice of the lord'.

Hand querns were not the only cause of offence. The Abbot of Bury St Edmunds had a windmill demolished because he claimed it infringed his manorial milling rights – incidentally, this is one of the earliest references to a windmill. One wonders how much progress in the development of other forms of power, has been hampered by the selfish protection of vested interests in the past, and even today.

There are a few references to a little freedom being allowed. In some cases 'freemen' might be allowed to take their corn to one of a number of mills, whereas villeins had no choice. Probably the vicar was another exception, since an inventory of standing furniture at Sturry Vicarage, prepared towards the end of the thirteenth century, included a hand mill – or would you rather draw other conclusions?

SOKE RIGHTS

Soke rights were built up over the years by tradition rather than by statute. In the same way, they did not come to an abrupt end by legislation. Instead they dwindled away, in some instances lingering on into the nineteenth century. More was involved than a simple right of the lord of the manor to expect his tenants to have their corn ground at his mill. His miller would take a proportion of the flour, usually known as multure. A multer bowl was used by some millers – taking one bowlful from every two bushels of grain – and the toll would be stored in the miller's ark or bin. The proportion was usually about a sixteenth, but it varied and there were devious ways in which the miller could take more than his due, leaving the tenant unable to do anything about it. Many court rolls refer to cases brought about by the dishonesty of a miller. Chaucer knew the situation well enough to describe the miller of Trumpington in Cambridgeshire, in about 1386, as

> a thief as well of corn and meal
> And sly at that; his habit was to steal.

An old rhyme makes a similar point, describing a miller with

> One hand in his pocket and other in his bag;
> As the wheel went round, he made his grab.

Only nine years after Chaucer had written *The Canterbury Tales*, there was an uproar in Chester from the citizens who objected to the tenant of the mill on the River Dee charging more than the one-sixteenth toll that they considered his due. They sent a petition to Richard II:

> To the xellent and or most redowbted sovereyne lord the Kyng. Youre pore leges and supplycants the meyre and comltie of yor citie of Chester showe that the mylners of yor milnes of dee do take from day to day divers owtragiouse partes over the right toll used throghe all yor realme of ther corne and malt over the xvj greyne after that it is grounde to the great ympoverishment and damage of yor said pore supplicants.
>
> That it mey please yor most highest majestie and of yor especiall grace to graunt unto theym to have ther corne and malt grounde at yr milnes for the xvj greyne without any other tole parte or any thyng over. For God sake and in love of the citie.

How could such a heartfelt plea go unheeded? The king ordered that a toll of one-sixteenth only should be taken for the next four years.

To make the situation more aggravating for a tenant, it could happen that he might find the miller busy, not a pleasant end to what may have been a lengthy and arduous journey. Still further difficulty might be caused by a lack of sufficient water, and there are references to tenants being required to wait for three days and nights before corn could be ground.

In order to enforce his rights, of course, the lord of the manor had to maintain his mill in good order. This was not so, however, in the case of the lord's mill at Forncett, south of Norwich, in 1279. It was producing very little, apparently because of 'its rickety condition', and since there were two newly built mills within reasonable distance, the freemen refused to use it. But in some places the landlord exercised the power to gain the assistance of tenants in maintaining a mill. At Guyzance Mill on the River Coquet in Northumbria, on one occasion, each tenant had to repair 8ft of the mill dam for each husbandland he held.

Then there were other difficulties, as the Prior of Monk Bretton had to accept in 1369, at his mill at Derfield in West Yorkshire. At one time his mill 'could and was wont to grind in a day and a night 4 quarters of any kind of corn', but then the building of another mill upstream had caused such a reduction in the flow of water that 'the mill cannot now grind in a day and a night more than one quarter of corn'. This is an interesting indication of the capacity of mills of that time and also highlights the problem of water rights, mentioned earlier, under the control of the Lord High Admiral, but only for navigable streams. His interest was in navigation and not in the miller – hence the change of control in 1422.

Soke rights and the power of the landlord were not confined to corn milling. By the end of the fifteenth century other uses of water-powered mills had become quite common. The fulling of cloth was one such use. Landowners were known to force weavers to send their cloth to the manorial mill, presenting small textile workers with a serious problem. Some were so seriously affected that they were unable to pay their annual guild dues, causing membership of the Guild of Weavers to fall to three-quarters of its earlier numbers.

In 1538, Sir Anthony Fitzherbert set down some of his observations on milling methods in a *Boke of Surveying and Improvements* (published posthumously). He explains that the custom of socorne (*soke regalis*) seems to apply to corn grown on the lord's land, in which case it must be ground at the lord's mill. But if the corn is bought in the market or elsewhere, then the corn can be ground wherever the best service is given.

Fitzherbert explains further:

> That manner of gryndyng is called Love Socone, and the lordes tenentes be called lorde Socone. And yf they grynd not thyr corne at the lordes mylne, the lord may amerce them in his court or els he may sue them at the common lawr . . . And it is also to be known how the tolle should be taken but there be so many dyverse grauntes made by the lorde, some men to be grounded to the twentie parte and some to the xxiij parte, some men to be tolle free, and some to be hopper free, that is to wyt, that his corne shall be put in the hopper and grounde next to the corne that is in the hopper, at the tyme of his comyng: and in some place to take the tolle after the strength of the water . . . And soo ther be soo many diversities of taking tolle that I shall not take uppon me to telle howe . . . But doubt ye not, the mylner wyll be no losers.

John Stow's *Survey of London*, written in 1558, adds more detail. He records that the miller should have a measure which has been assized and sealed to the King's Standard.

For the miller's toll

> he shall have of every Busshel of Whete a quart for the grinding if it be brought unto hym, and if he fetche it he shall have a quart for the grinding and anoder for the fetching . . . Also he shall not water nor change no manny's [man's] corne to give hym the worse for the better.

It could be that some crafty millers were tempted to take more than was due in order to feed a whole farmyard of animals, because Stow writes that the miller:

> shall have no Hogges, Gees [geese] nor duckes at his Mylle dore nor in his mylle of his owne nor of noon [none] oder mannys. Nor no mana of Pultre [poultry] but three Hennys and a Cok. And if he woll not be ware of two warnyng, then the third tyme he ys to be juged unto a Pillory.

IMPORTANT DEVELOPMENTS

THE EARLY INDUSTRIAL REVOLUTION

Slow but sure changes affecting watermills during the sixteenth and seventeenth centuries were heralded in John Stow's *London*. He was obviously aware of the growth of towns and the development of town mills. He gives some interesting details of the use of the Thames to drive corn mills erected under the arches of London Bridge. Along with the move to town life came the decline of the feudal system and a slow ending to the tyranny of soke rights. More millers became owners, if not of freehold, then of a lease for, say, twenty-one years. In other cases, a miller might pay an annual rent in cash, accepting full responsibility for the mill, including the maintenance of the stones in good order and their replacement when necessary.

The foundations of a capitalist-based industry were being laid. In France this was probably more noticeable: local citizens grouped together to establish companies. Building a new mill was comparatively expensive but a good investment. Joint ownership, consisting of between two and five parties, each usually taking an equal share of profits, became quite common at mill sites along the Seine in Paris. Of the situation in England, Stow observed:

> The profit of these Mills was, that whereas in time of Dearth the common People could not have any Corne ground under four, five or six Pence the Bushel, and many Times could not have it ground at all in a long Space (by Means whereof People were constrained to buy Meal in the Market at such Prices as the Seller himself would) this would be remedied by the Use of these Mills.

Rivers and streams could provide growing industry with a ready-made source of power and it is possible that at this time the number of mill sites was rising to a total approaching the peak reached in the eighteenth and nineteenth centuries. There were sixteen mills on the River Thames between Maidenhead and Oxford in 1579, according to Stow's account.

Further indications of developments can be obtained from what

Justice Fitzherbert wrote in 1538. He writes about ground or under-shot mills:

> ... the lorde may set divers maner of mylnes the which maye be to the Lordes great ease and profit. As upon the great ryvere corne mylnes that be called grounde mylnes because the overside of the headsyl lyeth even level with the over side of the grounde in the bottom of the water.

Then he provides information about building a head race and weir to supply water to a mill:

> And commonly these mylnes be not set upon the great stremes of the great ryvers, but a great part of the water is conveyed out of the great streme by a mylne streme made with mans hande to a certayne place, where wyse men thynke the mylne most convenient to be set and the seyd water to be holden up and broughte to the sed mylne by reason and setting of a weyre [weir] overthwart the seyd streme made of trouse [packed] tymber or stone or both.

He was also aware of the problem of backwatering:

> And when it is past the mylne, with a sufficient fall of the water that the mylne stand not in back water, to return to the ryver ageyn.

More on this problem later. Perhaps of greatest significance, Fitz-herbert was aware of all the main types of wheel:

> ... there be two maner of corne mylnes, that is to saye a braste mylne and overshot mylne, and these two maner of mylnes be set and goe most commonly upon small brookes and upon greate pooles and meryres and they have always a brode bowe a fote [foot] brode and more, and the ladles be always shrouded with compost bordes on both sydes to hold in the water, and then they be called buckettes. And they most be set moche nerer togyther than the ladels be, and moche more a slope down wardes to hold moche water that it fails not for it dryveth the wheel as well with the weight of the water as with the strengthe. And the mylner must drawe his water according to his buckettes, that they be always full and no more, for the longer that they holde the water the better they be.

From these accounts, it is clear that the main types of waterwheel were in use at least by the early sixteenth century. Fitzherbert makes the classification clear: when the water flows under the wheel, it is an *undershot* wheel, using the impulse or strength of the water – the type known and used since the time of Vitruvius; when the water flows over the wheel, dropping into buckets to turn the wheel by the weight of water, it is an *overshot* wheel; and if the water strikes the wheel at or about level with the centre of the wheel, it is referred to as a *breast* or *breastshot* wheel. A more detailed explanation of these types of wheel is given in Part Two.

BETTER COMMUNICATIONS

Another connection which was right for the development of the waterwheel was the introduction of printing. Hero's work *The Pneumatica* had been translated into Latin in Sicily during the twelfth century. But during the fifteenth century, the long-lost manuscript of *De Architectura* by Vitruvius was rediscovered at St Gall. In 1486, it was printed ten years after Caxton had returned from Bruges where he had learned Gutenburg's original method of printing.

At about the same time, Leonardo da Vinci produced sketches illustrating methods of transmission and transformation of movement. Many of his ideas for gearing in windmills and watermills, for lifting stones and for bearings, were in advance of contemporary thinking. They foreshadowed the gradual progress of the two or three centuries to follow, marking an end to the comparatively conservative approach of the previous two or three centuries during which millers had been content to follow a simple daily and annual routine. Means of communication were improving and so the rate of progress in increasing the efficiency of the waterwheel allowed more and more applications to be found.

There are some records of very early applications on the Continent. Water-driven hammers were operating at Schmidmühlen in Oberpfalz, Germany in 1010. The earliest fulling mill may have been in a village in Normandy in 1086 and a tanning mill is mentioned in connection with Notre-Dame, Paris, in 1138. Paper mills followed later, the first thought to have been at Xatira near Valencia in Spain about 1238. By 1268 there were seven paper mills working in Fabriano in Italy. French paper mills were known on the River Dore in 1326; one of them, Le Moulin à papier de Richard de Bas at Ambert in southeastern France, is still in operation.

The basic method of applying the power from the waterwheel to produce paper was one that has been much used ever since – a type of camshaft. The axle tree or shaft of the wheel extended across the side of the trough containing pulp. Projecting pieces of wood, mortised into the axle tree, formed the cams which lifted the ends of wooden levers as the wheel turned. Wooden stampers were mounted vertically on the levers and as the cams passed, the stamps dropped into the pulp in the trough below. The number of stamps and the number of cams to

1 An undershot wheel used in paper making. The cams or projections on the rotating axle tree (B) lift the ends of the levers, which in turn lift the wooden stampers (C) and allow them to fall on to the pulp in the troughs (F). From *Theatrum Machinarum Novum* by G. A. Böckler, 1662

each stamp for one revolution of the axle tree could vary according to the power of the wheel and the exact purpose of the mill.

In similar ways, this principle was applied in several industries. The tilt-hammer was known to fullers in the woollen trade for matting the material together, a process otherwise done by 'walking'. It was also used by the ironmasters of Kent and Sussex to forge the blooms for their furnaces. Small streams, however, could not always provide sufficient power to ensure that the hammers would not be 'held up' for lack of water, so hammer ponds were built to store it.

It was a significant step forward when the waterwheel took over the hard work of the smiths in forging steel blooms; the heavier blow and uniform stroke were much more efficient. Hammers might weigh from 1,100 up to 3,500lb, though for finer work, hammers of 660lb might be used at the rate of 60–120 strokes a minute. Finishing hammers of 150–180lb worked at about 200 strokes a minute.

By the middle of the sixteenth century, watermills in Britain were assisting in the main processes of mining and metal production including the operation of hammers and bellows, hoisting, crushing and stamping ore, mine ventilation, pumping and drawing wire. An undershot wheel is known to have been in use for wire drawing at Augsburg in 1351. It turned a crank attached to a rope and tongs held by a stirrup. The smith, squatting on a swing, was able to grasp the wire with the tongs and to move back as the crank drew the wire from the plate. Thus bellows were one of the most important applications of the water-wheel, providing sufficient draught to raise the temperature of a furnace to 1,500°C to melt iron ore. The first known water-powered bellows appeared in 1323, though the first real blast furnace was not developed until 1380.

If only printing methods and organisation had been better in the mid-sixteenth century, then Georgius Agricola might have seen the conclusion of his twenty-three years' work. Unfortunately, *De Re Metallica* (Plate 2 overleaf) appeared a year after his death in 1556 after being with the printer for five years. There are twelve volumes, but it is the sixth, on mining, that is the most interesting from a waterwheel point of view. He includes a description of mine pumps based on ideas used by the Egyptians and later the Saxons. The pumps were of the rag and chain type, driven by a waterwheel and used to lift water up to 250ft. They were designed to be built mainly of timber with a small amount of wrought iron.

Agricola's drawings show mainly overshot wheels, driving a series of drop-hammers for crushing ore, pumping, ventilating and winding. One shows a narrow but double wheel with the buckets of each half facing in opposite directions. The operator could, by means of a pivoted rod and levers, change the direction of the water to supply either series of buckets so that the wheel could turn in either direction.

A—Reservoir. B—Race. C, D—Levers. E, F—Troughs under the water gates.
G, H—Double rows of buckets. I—Axle. K—Larger drum. L—Drawing-chain.
M—Bag. N—Hanging cage. O—Man who directs the machine. P, Q—Men
emptying bags.

3 (*above*) An undershot wheel used for pumping water from a mine. From *Le Diverse et Artificose Machine* by Augustin Ramelli, 1588

2 The use of a waterwheel in sixteenth-century mining. The operator at 0 can direct water on to either of the twin overshot waterwheels according to the direction of rotation required to either raise or lower the bucket (M) in the mine shaft. From *De Re Metallica* by Georgius Agricola, 1556

A MORE SCIENTIFIC APPROACH

The efforts to develop a more efficient waterwheel and improve flour production were gathering momentum. Jerome Cordan produced *De Subtilitate* in 1550 in which he described the separation of flour and bran by the action of an agitated bolter or sieve. Then, again post-humously, a work by Jacques Besson, *Théâtre des instruments mathématiques et méchaniques*, was published in Lyons in 1578, ten years after it had been written; in it he described a mill with vertical shaft and curved blades, coming near to the design of a water turbine. Ten years later, an Italian engineer, Augustin Ramelli, wrote *Le Diverse et Artificose Machine*, which included similar ideas for a hori-zontal wheel with water carefully directed into spoon-shaped blades. But all the necessary connections were still not available to produce the turbine – there were 250 years to wait for that.

Within the next century or so, more published works appeared con-taining ideas which were the seeds of later applications in the In-dustrial Revolution. In 1607, in Padua, Italy, Vittorio Zonca's *Novo Teatro di Machine et Edificii* included drawings of undershot wheels showing clear details of a large wheel driving a lantern pinion attached to the main vertical shaft of the mill. He also showed a grind-stone revolving on edge, an idea to be much used for crushing instead of grinding. In addition, there were ideas for water-powered fulling stocks and a silk-throwing mill.

More ideas for improved flour production were shown by Veran-tius in *Machinae Novae* published in Venice in 1595. He described a method of mechanical bolting in which an inclined trough, covered with cloths of different meshes, was agitated. Similar ideas were devel-oped by the German engineer G. A. Böckler in *Theatrum Machin-arum Novum*, published in 1662. In addition to illustrating a paper mill, he describes a roller mill with an eccentric roller moving on a concave block. Meal was passed through a bolter agitated by a crank attached to the roller. It came very near to the modern mill, but in the event it was to take another 200 years for the idea to develop fully.

Jacob Leupold, who began to work as a cabinetmaker and then turned towards an ecclesiastical career, eventually showed his real interest by producing in 1724 a study of machines in nine volumes,

4 The use of an undershot wheel, driving the spur wheel (A) and the lantern pinion (B) to operate a stone for edge grinding. From *Novo Teatro di Machine et Edificii* by Vittorio Zonca, 1607

one of which, *Theatrum Machinarum Molarium*, included details of watermills and, in particular, methods of dressing stones.

JOHN SMEATON'S WATERWHEELS

An outstanding contribution to the development of the waterwheel as it moved towards its peak of efficiency, in Britain at least, was made by John Smeaton. The basis of his work was his carefully planned experiments on models during 1752–3. He prepared a paper – *An Experimental Enquiry concerning the Natural Power of Water and Wind to turn mills and other Machines depending on a circular motion* – which was presented to the Royal Society, of which he was a Fellow, after some delay while the conclusions were put into practice and proved valid.

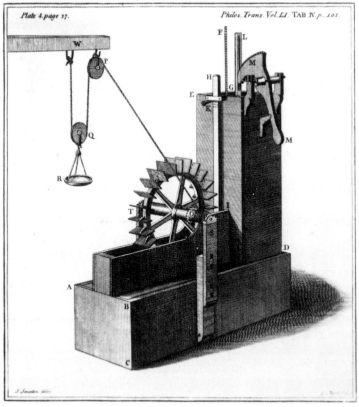

5 John Smeaton's drawing of his model apparatus for experiments on waterwheels

It had been realised for several hundred years that the effect of the *weight* of water in the buckets of an overshot wheel was greater than the *impulse* of water striking the paddles of an undershot wheel. Smeaton showed the difference scientifically and accurately, and used his findings to design the most effective wheel for any given situation. The deductions from his experiments were:

1. Concerning the Ratio between the Power and Effect of Overshot Wheels:
. . . the effect therefore of overshot wheels, under the same circumstances of quantity and fall, is at a medium double to that of the undershot: and as a consequence thereof, that nonelastic bodies, when acting by their impulse or collision, communicate only a part of their original power.
2. Concerning the most proper Height of the Wheel in proportion to the whole Descent:
. . . the higher the wheel is in proportion to the whole descent, the greater will be the effect; because it depends less upon the impulse of the head, and more upon the gravity of the water in the buckets.
. . . the water should have somewhat greater velocity, than the circumference of the wheel, in coming thereon; otherwise the wheel will not only be retarded, by the buckets striking the water, but thereby dashing a part of it over, so much of the power is lost.
3. Concerning the Velocity of the Circumference of the Wheel, in order to produce the greatest Effect:
. . . the slower a body descends, the greater will be the portion of the action of gravity applicable to the producing a mechanical effect.
. . . the best velocity for practice therefore will be such, as when the wheel here used made about 30 turns in a minute; that is, when the velocity of the circumference is a little more than 3 feet in a second.

This rule Smeaton applied to all sizes of overshot wheels though he acknowledged that larger wheels 'may deviate further from this rule, before they will lose their power'.

4. Concerning the Load for an Overshot Wheel, in order that it may produce a Maximum:
The maximum load for an overshot wheel, is that which reduces the circumference of the wheel to its proper velocity.'
5. Concerning the greatest possible Velocity of an Overshot Wheel:

Though this depends jointly on the diameter of the wheel and the velocity of the falling body, Smeaton argues that the body cannot fall through the semicircle (of the circumference) as fast as it would perpendicularly, ie according to gravity. Therefore, Smeaton surmised, 'the utmost velocity of overshot wheels is not to be determined generally'.

It is of no great consequence in producing the effect required.

> 6. Concerning the greatest Load that an Overshot Wheel can overcome:
> . . . as the buckets may be of any given capacity, the more the wheel is
> loaded, the slower it turns; but the slower it turns, the more will the
> buckets be filled with water; and consequently tho' the diameter of the
> wheel, and quantity of water expended, are both limited . . . the greatest
> load an overshot wheel will overcome, considered abstractedly, is unlimi-
> ted.

Smeaton realised that 'when we really go to work to build a wheel' (what a delightful phrase!) there comes a point when a wheel is loaded so much that its motion becomes irregular: 'yet this never happens till the velocity of the circumference is less than 2 feet per second.'

In conclusion, Smeaton refers to the 'several kinds of breastwheels' when the impulse and weight of the water are combined. The principles involved therefore are combinations of those already given:

> the effect of such a wheel will be equal to the effect of an undershot, whose
> head is equal to the difference of level between the surface of the water in
> the reservoir and the point where it strikes the wheel, added to that of an
> overshot, whose height is equal to the difference of level, between the point
> where it strikes the wheel and the level of the tail-water.

The wheel should receive the impulse at right angles to its radius, and the velocity of the circumference should be in accordance with principles already given.

From his experiments, Smeaton obtained 22 per cent efficiency from an undershot wheel and 63 per cent from an overshot wheel. Although he had found just over 3 feet per second to be an efficient circumferential speed of buckets, he often used up to 6 feet per second which gave a rotational speed of nearly 6rpm for a 20ft diameter wheel.

Smeaton began to put his theories into practice in 1753 when he designed Halton flour mill, near Warrington. His practice was to refer to the use of waterwheels for driving pumps or furnace blowers as 'engines' and others for grinding various materials and for fulling as 'mills'. Later in 1753 came the Ridge Wood engine and the Honeycomb Great engine. In the following year, he designed a flour mill at Wakefield with a low breast wheel 20ft in diameter and 6ft 8in wide. By 1761 he was engaged to build Colchester fulling mill and then Hounslow Heath copper mill, both with low breast wheels.

Perhaps Smeaton's greatest contribution to the use of waterpower was at the Carron ironworks in Stirling. He was first engaged in 1764 and continued to have interests there until 1785, building several furnace blowers with high breast and overshot wheels, a boring mill with two low breast wheels for boring cylinders and gun barrels, and a clay mill with two low breast wheels. He had realised that the timber shaft of a wheel created difficulties and in 1769, for one of the Carron furnaces, he fitted what was probably the first cast-iron shaft. Later, as the difficulties of large castings were overcome, wheels with complete iron frames became common, with timber used for paddles or buckets.

In 1765, at the Kilnhurst forge near Rotherham, Smeaton installed six low breast wheels to drive tilt- and trip-hammers with an additional wheel to drive a slitting mill. One of his largest wheels was the undershot wheel for the London Bridge engine designed in 1768 – 32ft in diameter and 15ft 6in wide. In contrast to that, in the following year he used a wheel only 7ft in diameter and 1ft 6in wide to power the Thoresby engine in Nottinghamshire. During 1771, two fairly similar low breast wheels were used for gunpowder mills at Waltham Abbey in Essex and at Hounslow Heath.

It is worth noting that in the same year, Arthur Young recorded that English farming had improved so much since 1600 that the average yield of corn had trebled to around 24 bushels per acre. There was obviously more work for the watermills – assisted by windmills of course – and their builders to do. In the next decade, Smeaton was responsible for mills for flour, flock, fulling, paper and snuff, and for the oil and bark mill at Carshalton, where he not only used a cast-iron axle but also replaced wooden boards with wrought-iron plates for buckets, thereby increasing their capacity.

The 15ft diameter overshot wheel for the Thornton paper mill in Fife is interesting since it is the only example with curved arms. Scremerston grist mill, near Berwick-upon-Tweed, built in 1776, was also unique since it had a horizontal wheel and was in fact almost a turbine. In 1781 Smeaton was the 'civil engineer' engaged in the building of a large corn mill for HM Victualling Yard at Deptford; its overshot wheel provided sufficient power to drive three pairs of stones, grinding 90 tons of corn a week. This was one of Smeaton's most important achievements, and is particularly interesting because the site did not provide a natural supply of water. It was an example of the early application of the Newcomen atmospheric steam engine, used to return water from the tail race below the wheel to enter the wheel again along the head race. Four years earlier, the idea had been successfully used by Matthew Boulton, partner to James Watt, at their

Soho works, then two miles from Birmingham. 'Old Bess', the steam engine built there, pumped water from tail race to head race when the natural supply of water was inadequate to drive the 24ft diameter wheel.

Also in 1781, Smeaton designed one of his smallest wheels – a 4ft diameter overshot wheel at Welbeck in Nottinghamshire. When he was over sixty, he made good use of the site for Alston grist mill, Cumberland, in designing a 30ft diameter overshot wheel. Many will know and respect Smeaton for his designs for bridges, for harbours such as St Ives and, of course, for the Eddystone lighthouse. But his work on waterwheels, and its effect during the Industrial Revolution, deserves at least equal praise.

OTHER ENGINEERS

Andrew Meikle was one of Smeaton's contemporaries. His grandfather had been the first to introduce iron founding into Scotland, and his father, a millwright, had produced the first winnowing machine in Scotland after visiting Holland to study agricultural machinery. Andrew was brought up and worked at Houston Mill in East Lothian and is best known for his invention of the threshing machine in 1787. He passed his engineering skills on to his son George, but it so happened that another young man, John Rennie, lived near enough to pay frequent visits to the Meikle workshop while a schoolboy.

Within five years of leaving Edinburgh University, Rennie was putting those early practical experiences and his academic studies together in building the Albion Mills near Blackfriars Bridge in London, powered by two 50hp Boulton and Watt steam engines. The significant point here is that by improved methods of grinding and dressing, 4½ tons of corn could be ground in an hour, thus reducing the price of flour to make it available to a wider public. Unfortunately, the mill was burnt down after running for only three years. Rennie made a substantial improvement to the breast wheel by adding a sliding hatch mechanism – a curved iron gate, operated by a rack and pinion – to control the head of water and thus obtain greater efficiency.

No account of the development of milling would be complete without reference to the work of Oliver Evans, an American engineer who was regarded by some of his contemporaries, at times, as something of a crank. But despite early opposition, he introduced many ideas into corn milling and the production of cotton which were considerable improvements to both industries. He introduced labour-saving devices such as elevators to lift grain and rotating augers to transport grain along wooden troughs. The *Young Millwright and Miller's Guide*, which he wrote in about 1780, gives clear and well illustrated details of such ideas. In Britain, his methods were adopted more slowly.

When John Sutcliffe produced his 'Instructions for Designing and Building a Corn Mill and How to Grind Corn upon the Best Principle' in 1816 (contained in *A Treatise on Canals and Reservoirs*), he was obviously still concerned about the disputes that had for so long marred the peace of the mill owner:

> Every mill owner should ascertain the fall if any from the crown of the weir next below him and the centre stone in the wheel race next above him and have the levels engraved upon a strong copper plate . . . or law suits will most certainly take place.

REACHING A PEAK

Still more improvement, this time to the undershot wheel, was made by General J. V. Poncelet. He had served under Napoleon and was an outstanding mathematician and engineer. Working on the principle that the water must enter and leave the wheel with little shock for greatest efficiency, he channelled the water to flow under an adjustable iron sheet and strike the accurately curved paddles of the wheel. The water then fell into a lower tail race to avoid the possibility of backwatering. These Poncelet wheels, as they became known, came into use about 1824 and were much used during the nineteenth century. One erected in 1849 near Montserrat in Catalonia, Spain, was outstandingly efficient. With only 6ft 6in head of water, it was capable of developing 180hp.

This, however, was not the peak of watermill perfection. The credit for this should almost certainly go to Sir William Fairbairn. His concern was not so much with obtaining the maximum power from a given supply of water, but rather with making sure that as little as possible was wasted. Some millers used to talk of the wheel becoming 'tail-bound', or of backwatering, by which they meant the resistance caused by water not clearing the wheel quickly in the tail race. Fairbairn wrote:

> The wheel should always be placed above the tail-water and not be carried down to the level of the tail-race floor as in older wheels and the breast of wood, iron or stone, which is of so much importance for low falls in retaining the water on the wheel, should break off about 10 inches from the extremity of a vertical diameter of the wheel.

He also realised that in larger wheels, loss of power could be due to air being trapped in the buckets which would, therefore, not be as full as possible and not provide the maximum weight to turn the wheel. To overcome this, he introduced ventilated buckets so that air could be forced out and allow water to enter more quickly. When the buckets reached the bottom, air could re-enter and assist in emptying them more quickly. Fairbairn claimed that his improvement increased the efficiency of the wheel by 25 per cent.

In 1827 he was employed as a very young engineer to power the textile mills for Finlay and Co at Catrine in Ayrshire. He designed two 250hp wheels, each 50ft in diameter and 10ft wide, and geared to shafting which transmitted the power throughout two multi-storey mills. They remained in continuous use for 120 years before being replaced by electricity. What valiant service!

At Deanston in Perth, four wheels, 37ft in diameter and 12ft wide and each developing 75hp, were built in 1830 and also served for nearly 120 years. Wheels of that size had to revolve only twice per minute and consequently, wear was not great. Much later, Fairbairn set down his theories and achievements in *A Treatise on Mills and Millwork* which provides full details of the Catrine mills.

Sir Marc Isambard Brunel (1769–1849) was responsible for saw-mills at Dartford and Chatham dockyards. They had undershot wheels which had iron axles and were 16ft in diameter and 4ft 6in wide. Another contributor to waterwheel design was civil engineer Joseph Glynn who wote *On the Power of Water to turn Mills* in 1853. He accepted much of Smeaton's theories but in general used higher peripheral speeds. He also placed greater emphasis on limits to the diameter of overshot wheels because larger wheels were cumbersome, slow and too expensive to produce.

Ironically, at about the same time that Poncelet, Fairbairn and others were bringing the waterwheel to its height of efficiency, Benoît Fourneyron was, in about 1824, working on the development of the water turbine, which was really a progression from the horizontal wheel – back to where the story began, a full circle!

GRINDING TO A HALT

An Interval
During Which
The Watermill Scene Changes

The advent of the water turbine was one factor that contributed to the ending of the waterwheel's glory and some, quite naturally, were not sorry. A contributor to Abraham Ree's *Cyclopedia* wrote in 1819:

> As mills of this kind often form and oppose great obstructions to different improvements of the farmer, and especially in the practice of watering land, they should consequently be diminished in number as much as possible . . . and those of the tide and wind kinds substituted in their place.

A large proportion of waterwheels had, of course, been used for corn grinding and this type of mill was affected most. Not that the mill was no longer used – many changed to other uses. An interesting example is the Rutter Force Mill on Hoff Beck, just south of Appleby in Cumbria, which worked as a corn mill until the 1850s. It then became a bobbin-turning mill in 1858, continuing as such until 1894, when it changed to a sawmill. Then in the 1930s it operated as the Great Asby Electric Light Co Ltd. It is now used as a barn.

Another event that affected the flour mills was the repeal of the Corn Laws in 1846. As a result, grain and flour could be imported duty-free, coming largely, at first, from Austria and Hungary. Imports rose from under 80,000 tons in 1840 to over 250,000 tons twenty years later. Quantities of that order were bound to affect the situation in small mills in this country.

There were other difficulties ahead for the small-scale millers. Continental millers were developing the technique of a reducing process which was claimed to improve quality and produce white flour. Country millers found it very difficult to cope with the competition and demand. Many were forced to close down or restrict themselves to grist mills for animal feed, as some still do. The use of rollers for milling had been introduced as early as the sixteenth century by Ramelli. There were also some references to rollers in the seventeenth and eighteenth centuries, but it was not until the mid-nineteenth century that any large-scale attempts were made, at first in conjunction with stones. Continental methods were not rapidly accepted in Britain but, by about 1890, many small mills were replaced by large mills like Whitworth's, powered by steam engines or, in other cases, by water turbines.

Concern for public health, including the improvement of drinking-water supplies and the provision of 'water closets', made greater demands on water reserves. Growing industries increased their requirements and so placed the utmost strain on water boards; in some cases, streams supplying mills were robbed of water, and in others they disappeared completely. Water boards were compelled to increase stocks and it was in the construction of Broomhead Reservoir, for example, that a mill was submerged – what had been its life-blood became the murder weapon for one of the two mills at Bradfield.

Worse, perhaps, was the lingering death of Flelland Mill on the River Glen in the parish of Milsthorpe. Samuel Chatterton, the miller, opposed the Peterborough Water Bill in 1875, his solicitors claiming that: 'if the waters of Bracebridge Spa stream are taken and impounded as proposed his said mill will for considerable periods of the year be incapable of being worked.' The Peterborough Water Company offered £3,500 to Chatterton to be paid as soon as water was abstracted after giving two months' notice of the day, on condition that the miller withdraw his petition and 'shall not further oppose the bill'. Samuel Chatterton, it appears, gave in and claimed £29 1s 0d for his expenses. Sometime later, however, his solicitors showed that when the mill was sold 'there be a mortgage of £5,000 but the mortgagees accepted £2,300 because it had become out of repair, unoccupied and all trade gone'.

The remains of a seventeenth-century blast furnace, once used for smelting iron and driven by a waterwheel, have been buried under Staunton Harold Reservoir which has been supplying the City of Leicester's water since 1963. Bilberry fulling mill, part of a sizeable woollen industry at one time near Holme in Yorkshire was lost when Digley Reservoir was constructed. There must be several more that have gone in a similar way.

The construction of the railways went on relentlessly in the latter half of the nineteenth century with no respect for any humble mill that happened to be in the way. The mill at Wharren Percy in East Yorkshire is only one which we know to have been lost in this manner. Motorway construction is the more recent axe to fall on at least one more watermill – that at Lower Roughwood, Hassall Green, near Sandbach in Cheshire. Though still standing complete with all its machinery when last seen, it has been completely robbed of its water supply by the building of the M6.

During World War II and the campaign to collect all available scrap metal for the manufacture of weapons and essential goods, wheels and machinery that were standing idle and appeared to have come to the end of their useful lives were seen as a source of supply. A few mills disappeared in this way.

And what a cruel ending for the once picturesque mill at Hardingham in Norfolk: during 1966 it was purposely burnt down for the shooting of a scene in the film *The Shuttered Room.*

Part Two

How a Watermill Works

WATER SUPPLY AND CONTROL

RIVERS AND STREAMS

Choosing a site is critical for the success of a mill and much depends on the local landscape. The Saxons were good at selecting suitable sites; manorial and monastic landlords who followed added many more. It would be most interesting, if it was ever possible, to find the greatest number of sites in use at any particular time. It may be that well over 10,000 different sites in Britain have been used at one time or another.

The stream supplying water to a mill is usually known as the leat or sometimes the head race. In early mills, this could be achieved by building a causeway or fixed weir, sometimes referred to in old records as the 'low-shottes'. Surplus water would fall over this and bypass the wheel. The disputes that arose when some mill owners attempted to raise the level of a weir to obtain more water have already been mentioned.

6 Sluice control gear at Belton Mill, Leicestershire

The simplest method of obtaining power, if the site was right, was to use the natural fall of the river or stream. The mill building would be placed alongside the original stream, then an artificial channel was excavated to bypass the mill. Water entering this was controlled by a sluice and adjusted by the miller according to the weather conditions and anticipated workload. Every site is different, of course, and there are several variations on the basic plan. The building could be on the opposite side of the stream from the sluice, in which case there would be a bridge over the tail race and a footpath to the sluice control. The distances might vary considerably according to the natural contours and the miller's convenience.

Another variation, used where the flow of water was greater, was to build the wheel across part of the width of the stream with a sluice controlling the supply of water to the wheel. A second sluice controlled the bypass water running alongside the wheel and into the tail race. Larger mills might be built to straddle the stream completely; bypass water would pass through a second arch under the mill and into the tail race.

A different method was to build up an embankment on either side of a stream and create a millpond. With skill and care, a miller could use sluices to ensure that the pond was a store of power. The windmiller could not do that! A sluice or weir would be required to regulate the supply of water coming into the pond and to avoid flooding, allowing surplus water to flow past the mill. On a derelict site, the height of the embankments and weir can provide an indication of the size of wheel used. Inside the mill would be the control that regulated the water flowing on to the wheel itself.

For a third method, a channel or leat was cut along rising ground or a hillside, directing water to fall on to the wheel. When not required for turning the wheel, the water would flow out of the leat, at a sluice control, and rejoin the stream. It would also be possible, in some cases, to arrange a combination of a millpond and a leat to supply the wheel. This would be a suitable arrangement where the best site for a pond and the best site for a mill building were some distance apart, as for example at Arkwright's Mill in Cromford, still to be seen, where water has to travel a considerable distance from the reservoir along a pipe to the wheel.

The building of a weir needed careful planning and construction. For moderate-sized rivers, a V-form dam across the river bed was preferred since this would spread the fall of water over a large surface and diminish the destructive effects on the apron below and on the banks of the river. The most effective type of weir for a stream was one built of solid ashlar stone, formed on the arc of a circle across the stream.

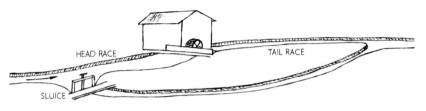

EXTERNAL WHEEL. MILL BUILT ON MAIN
STREAM OR ON LEAT

HEAD RACE

TAIL RACE

SLUICE

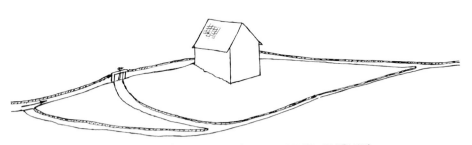

'ISLAND' MILL. FLOODGATE SOMETIMES CONDUCTS
WATER AWAY UNDERGROUND

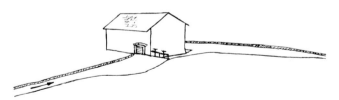

INTERNAL WHEEL. BYPASS WATER RUNS
PARALLEL TO THE WHEEL

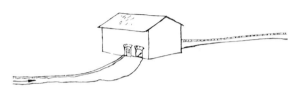

'STRADDLE' MILL, BUILT OVER THE STREAM

Fig 2   Some arrangements of watercourses

Where plenty of timber was available, an open timber frame was built, with large boulder stones, resting on gravel, packed into it. If timber was really plentiful, a series of timber steps might be built. The top of the weir, the sill, would be capped with flat stones.

TIDE MILLS

A unique source of power for a waterwheel is that obtained from the tide. Though suitable sites may be more limited than one might think, the idea has been used quite extensively and over a long period. A reference in the Domesday survey to a mill 'at the entrance to the port of Dover' presumably means a tidal mill.

Crashe Mills at Wapping, belonging to the Priory of Holy Trinity, Aldgate, in the thirteenth century, were tidal, as was the monastic mill of Westminster Abbey. A lease of 1475 mentions 'the stream flowing and reflowing from the mill of the said monastery to the Totehill'. It had an undershot wheel and was used for grinding corn. Floodgates were necessary and when, in 1678, the mill had fallen into disuse, flooding became troublesome. In 1526, a causeway was constructed across Stonehouse Pool near Plymouth, impounding water on high tides and releasing it through three arches to work the mill on ebb tides. The country's first water-powered gunpowder works was a tide mill on the River Ravensbourne, an old tributary of the Thames and used by Henry Reve in 1554. When he allowed nearby marshland to become flooded, it was discovered that he had no right to either mill or land!

Tide mills received a burst of enthusiasm when, in 1760, the Society of Arts offered awards for improved designs. Early entries, however, were not thought to be outstanding, but in 1761 a full award was made to the Rev H. Gainsborough of Henley who suggested:

1. a wheel 2ft in diameter, having ten floats held by means of a double lever and chains so that it could be raised and lowered with the tide.
2. float guides, adjustable to any degree from high to low water.
3. an arrangement at head and tail race for a fall of water to each, bypassing the wheel if not required.
4. a lantern pinion sliding as required from the upper to the under side of the crown wheel. The stones [and there were to be two pairs] could then turn the same way at all times, whichever way the water wheel was turning according to ebb or flow tides.
5. a false bottom board or fence, raised or lowered with the wheel to convey dead water away by a sort of whirlpool.

A tide mill built in Liverpool in 1796 worked for nearly thirty years before being demolished for dock extensions. Its designer, a Mr Jackson, worked on the principle of dividing the full height of the tide into three equal parts: one third for the upper reservoir, one for the fall in the wheel and one for the lower reservoir.

No account of tide mills, even if as brief as this, could justifiably omit to mention the Three Mills Distillery at Bromley-by-Bow, now a scheduled building and owned by the Lea Valley Regional Park Authority. After a long history as a flour mill, it was converted to distilling in 1727 when sold to Peter Lefevre, and has continued that trade ever since, though more recently it has been used as a bonded warehouse for bottling and storage. Its power and capacity were outstanding. In a survey of 1872, the Clock Mill is shown as having ten pairs of French burr stones, six pairs driven by three undershot wheels. Two of the wheels were made of iron – one 20ft in diameter and 3ft 9in wide, one 20ft in diameter and 2ft 6in wide – and the third was wooden, 16ft in diameter and 4ft wide. The House Mill had eight pairs of French stones driven by four undershot wheels – one 16ft in diameter and 3ft wide, and three 18ft in diameter and 12ft wide. Some of the gearing is made of ilex oak, an evergreen variety that withstands wet conditions well.

Tide mills, or what remains of them, are likely to be found along the tidal sections of rivers, particularly among the low-lying tidal creeks near the coastline of Cornwall, Devon, Hampshire, the Isle of Wight and Sussex in the south, Essex and Suffolk in the east, and Pembrokeshire in South Wales. A feature of most of them is a very large pond. At Birdham in Sussex, for example, the pond covered 13 acres with a smaller reserve pond in addition. In the dam across the creek, the sluice gates would open by the pressure of the incoming tide, allowing the pond to fill. When the tide turned, the pressure of water in the pond closed the gates and the water was directed through the mill. (This was the common method, but Fairbairn describes a mill in the Ionian Islands worked by an incoming tide.)

To work round the clock, a mill had either two wheels or two gates to one wheel. When the pond was at its fullest and the force of water greatest, the wheel could operate as a breast wheel. As the level of water fell, the flow of water could be directed to an undershot wheel. Alternatively, by opening a second sluice or gate at the bottom, the flow of water could be lowered to operate the same wheel as an undershot type.

Since the time of high tide moves each day, the times of working could be rather inconvenient for a miller. No two days together would be quite the same and, depending on the type of mill and the amount of work on hand, he might have to start or finish work at the oddest hour. At Birdham, work normally began 3½ hours after high tide and continued for 5½ hours; it was limited to two periods of this length per day. This mill had two wheels, one of iron, 12ft 6in in diameter and 4ft 9in wide, and one of wood, 11ft 6in in diameter and 7ft wide. Mr Farne, the owner, used to claim he could grind eight sacks of wheat per hour on one pair of stones at Birdham before work ceased in 1935.

The construction of a reserve millpond was usually undertaken at sites where neap tides left a shortage of water. But the other extreme caused the millers more concern. The time when the whole mill shook violently one night is related by J. Bryant. As a lad, he and a fellow-worker at Barron Hill Mill in Essex were so frightened that they left the mill. Next morning they discovered the explanation: a school of porpoises had dived after fish at high tide and come up under the mill floor.

Tide milling must have been worthwhile, at least to some millers. William Catt, tenant of the Duke of Newcastle's tidal mill at Bishop-stone in Sussex, made a fortune of half a million pounds at the mill in the early nineteenth century.

FLOATING MILLS

One further method of obtaining a water supply is by the relatively simple idea of a floating mill. The head race and tail race are parts of the stream or river, with no need for any excavations. This method is believed to have originated in AD 536 when Rome was besieged by the Ostrogoths. They cut the Trojan aqueduct, threatening the Romans with starvation since there was no water to drive the mill. General Belisarius harnessed a series of barges in pairs, by means of hawsers stretched across the river, with a waterwheel between each pair. This was geared to stones mounted on the barges. It was a successful idea and one used later in several large European towns.

There are records of floating mills on the Tigris near Baghdad in the tenth century, which were used for paper making. In Venice a century or so later, they were called 'boat mills', and took advantage of the ebb and flow of the tide by changing position every six hours. One built on the Seine in Paris under the Grand Pont worked for over a century before being destroyed with the bridge in 1296; however, an illustrated manuscript of 1317 shows a floating mill on the Seine, and in 1323 there were thirteen floating mills in the area. An outstanding location was the Garonne in France. Before the middle of the twelfth century there were more than sixty floating mills; then the Toulouse

7 Paddle wheels used to operate a floating mill, *c* 1590

millwrights built large dams and, with a flow of over 1,200 cu ft of water per second, it was a powerful site.

The Loire near Orléans, the Danube and the Po rivers were all used at some time for floating mills, and a woodcut of 1499 shows them in use in Cologne harbour. There are references to mills on the Thames in the sixteenth and eighteenth centuries, but they do not appear to have been particularly successful. In Lyons, however, it was quite different; floating mills supplied the city with flour in the eighteenth century. More recently, the principle has been widely used in Hungary. As elsewhere, of course, though the idea is a simple one, its basic difficulty had to be overcome – that of danger and handicap to shipping and other river-users. The Hungarians used guard boats, stationed a good distance both upstream and downstream of the mill boat, to warn and hold up approaching boats until it was possible to stop the mill, remove the harness and allow traffic through.

One can imagine some of the difficulties and hazards: Not only were the mills annoying to river traffic, but there was also a serious risk of a boat breaking loose in heavy water, crashing into other boats and damaging river banks. Part of the problem could be overcome by harnessing the boats across one arch of a bridge, leaving other arches free for traffic. But this method had its difficulties, as was found in London: the force of water cut a deep channel in the bed of the river forming the head race to the wheel, and began to undermine the foundations of the bridge's stone piers.

TYPES OF WATERWHEEL

The main classification of waterwheels is made according to the position of the main shaft, whether vertical or horizontal. Alternatively, the same distinction may be made by looking at the plane in which the wheel revolves – a more common method. Thus the very simple Norse mill, with a vertical shaft, has a horizontal wheel, while those developed from the Vitruvian type, with a horizontal shaft, have vertical wheels. Further classification is made by considering the position of the water in relation to the wheel. For vertical wheels, the water may flow over the wheel or under it – hence the descriptions overshot and undershot wheels. If the water reaches the wheel between these extremes, then the exact point will further define the wheel.

Though it is not normally used to classify types of wheel, it is important to be aware of the kind of energy being used. Water can be used in three ways:

1. for its potential energy because of its position; water stored and then allowed to fall to fill the buckets and turn the wheel by its weight, is using this energy.
2. for its kinetic energy due to velocity.
3. for its pressure energy due to increased pressure in a closed pipe.

HORIZONTAL WHEELS

The Norse horizontal wheel, originating from the Greek mill, is a very simple, relatively inefficient form of machine, but one that has, in the past, served many a small community by producing sufficient flour for local needs. These wheels have been found wherever Norsemen have travelled, with some of the oldest remains located in Ireland. Some evidence of their use in England has been found, and further north – particularly in the Western Isles of Scotland and the Orkneys and Shetlands – they were quite a common local feature. In 1814, Sir Walter Scott found that 'there are about 500 such mills in Shetland, each capable of grinding more than a sack at a time'. Though the type of wheel has been known for many centuries, some believe that its existence in these remote areas may go back less than three centuries.

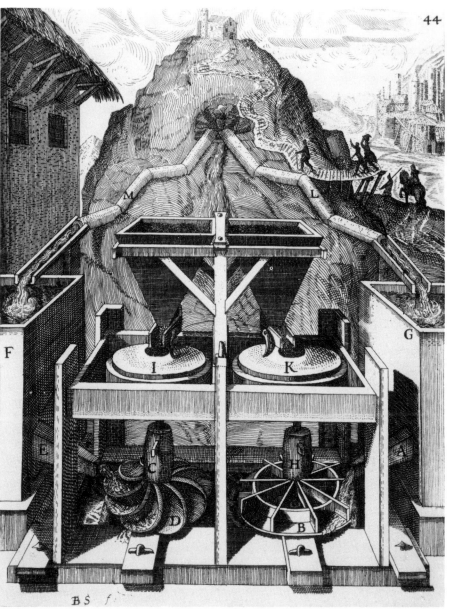

8 Two designs for mills driven by horizontal wheels. The one on the right shows a similarity with the original Greek mill, and the one on the left how closely the idea approached the nineteenth-century water turbine. From *Theatrum Machinarum Novum* by G. A. Böckler, 1662

Most of the wheels were constructed entirely of wood. The blades, which could be flat and set at various angles or shaped in a variety of ways, were fixed into mortises in a boss or nave attached to the bottom of the vertical shaft of iron or wood. In the remotest areas, any available timber was used, but parts found in Ireland have usually been made of oak with occasional examples of yew. Wheels in northern Britain normally had between four and twelve blades; these were left completely open with an obvious loss of efficiency as water escaped at the periphery. Better wheels were shrouded; a rim or shroud of wood or iron around the outer edges of the blades reduced water loss and so increased efficiency slightly, though it was probably done more to strengthen the wheel.

Horizontal wheels on the Continent and in the Middle East have been found to be more sophisticated, particularly in the design of the blades, some of which are spoon-shaped and approaching the principle of the Pelton wheel which was to supersede the waterwheel. Continental wheels are frequently larger in diameter and have a greater number of blades.

In mills in the Scottish Isles, water was diverted from a stream – where there was a head or fall of water of about 4ft – along a wooden trough which was usually inclined at an angle of between 20° and 40°. This would be directed on to a point on the blades near the circumference of the wheel to achieve the maximum force from the velocity of the water. In other areas, various ideas were employed to build up pressure and therefore obtain a more powerful jet of water, even to the extent of fitting different sizes of nozzles on the end of a pipe. An especially interesting idea has been used in Israel where the pressure has been obtained by building a water tower, the Aruba Penstock. From the stream, water is channelled to the top of the tower and is then forced out at the bottom to be directed on to the horizontal wheel.

Operation of a horizontal mill
Before looking at other types of waterwheel, it will be more appropriate to complete a description of the working of a horizontal mill since its operation, with no gearing or other machinery, was much simpler than that of other mills.

Below the wheel, or tirl as it was frequently known, the end of the vertical shaft was held in a pivot bearing often fixed to a beam called the sole tree. The top of the shaft passed through the floor, through the bottom, fixed millstone (bedstone), which might have had a simple bush (the grutte) for smoother running, and into the upper, revolving stone (runner stone). This stone revolved at the same speed as the tirl since it was connected to the shaft. This was achieved by using a short iron bar, usually curved, which was sunk into the underside of the runner stone, across its eye, in the centre. Known as the rynd (or sile in the Shetlands), the bar rested on the top of the shaft which was sometimes made square to fit a similar hole in the rynd.

For good grinding, the upper stone had to be well balanced, since the vertical shaft took all its weight. Adjustment of the gap between the stones could be achieved by means of a wedge in a slot in the top of the lightening tree – part of the wooden framework which was pivoted to the sole tree at the bottom and passed through the grinding floor. The wedge could adjust the whole framework, including the tirl and the runner stone. By this means the flour could be 'lightened'. The hopper containing the grain was often rather crudely slung from the roof timbers; the grain was directed from it along a spout into the eye of the upper stone. A continuous supply could be ensured by using a clapper resting on the upper stone and attached by a piece of string or twig to the spout.

Stones had to be rather limited in size because of the direct drive. They were often 18in in diameter, and seldom more than 36in. A stone of 30in diameter, fed by a 4ft fall of water, would turn at about 50rpm, developing just under 1hp and having an average output of 40–50lb an hour. At some small mills, the hopper size and the flow of water were often about right for the mill to be left running overnight to produce a sack full of flour by the next morning.

VERTICAL WHEELS

Stream wheel
Not particularly efficient in mechanical terms, stream wheels are the simplest form of vertical wheel in both construction and operation. They rely entirely on the impulse of the stream to turn them, and therefore the right kind of location, such as a mountain stream, is required. Consequently, they have been more commonly found in other countries than in Britain. The wheel consists of flat wooden paddles, usually about 10–15in deep. Depending on the locality, there can be times when the flow of water is inadequate or even when the stream dries up completely. At the other extreme, of course, work can be held up if the stream is frozen.

An improvement was sometimes made by levelling out the stream above the wheel to raise the level of the water a little. It then flowed down a steeper spillway to strike the paddles with slightly greater force and pass under the wheel. This is then approaching the undershot wheel.

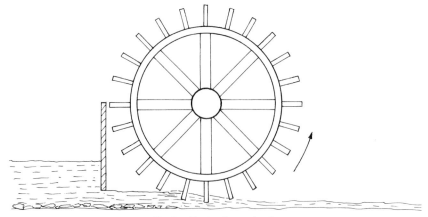

Fig 3   Undershot wheel

Undershot wheel

Smeaton showed that the undershot wheel had a relatively low efficiency of 22 per cent, but such wheels have nevertheless been much used and there are examples to be found still in working order. The wheel is turned by the kinetic energy of the water as it strikes the paddles at a height not greater than between 7 and 8 o'clock with the water flowing from the left.

9 Undershot wheel with paddles at Skenfrith, Gwent, on the River Monnow

A hatch or control gate may be used to hold back the water which then flows underneath the wheel, according to the requirements of the miller. Improvements can be made in the care with which the water is directed on to the wheel. Shrouding will reduce loss of water at the sides. Paddles are rather more efficient if made not from a single board but from two, set edge to edge with an obtuse angle between them, thus producing a scoop-like effect. Too much water in the tail race as it leaves the wheel can cause resistance to the paddles, known as backwatering; if a slight fall can be arranged in the tail race, this may help to reduce the defect. This point has already been referred to and was one of the improvements made in the Poncelet wheel.

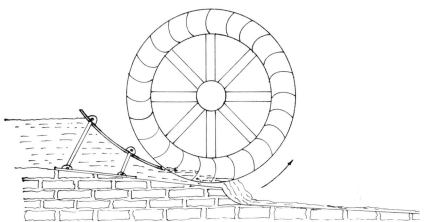

Fig 4 Poncelet type of undershot wheel

Poncelet wheel

The French engineer General J. V. Poncelet gave the undershot wheel a new lease of life, claiming that its efficiency was increased to 65 per cent. His type of wheel is easily recognised, first by looking at the control gate. The earlier vertical hatch on the undershot wheel was replaced by one inclined at between 40° and 60° to the horizontal, according to the diameter of the wheel and the effective head of water. About 5ft 6in was recommended for this. A false board held back a head of water at the top while the bottom gate could be adjusted by means of a hand wheel, spur gear and rack for 6–7in to control the amount of water going on to the wheel. This was frequently constructed so that adjustments could be made from inside the mill.

The second point to look for is the improved design of the paddles –

almost buckets but not enclosed. They were inclined at a tangent so
that the water entered without shock, using velocity only to turn the
wheel. The radius of the 'buckets' was usually about one-eighth of the
diameter of the wheel, and they had no sole plate or bottom. This
shape allowed them to glide out of the tailwater with less resistance.
Finally, there should be a fall on the tail race just beyond the centre
line of the wheel, to avoid backwatering.

Poncelet introduced his wheel in about 1824, a useful date to
remember when endeavouring to establish the date of a mill or at least
its wheel. One of the first manufacturers in this country is believed to
have been Maggs and Hindley of Bourton Foundry, Dorset.

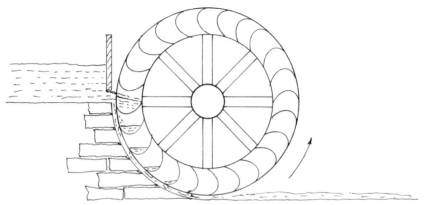

Fig 5   Breast or breastshot wheel

Breast or breastshot wheel
We now turn to wheels that are driven by the *weight* of water, and
therefore find wheels with buckets designed ideally to hold as much
water as possible, for as long as possible. The term breastshot covers
quite a range of wheels. Basically, it describes a wheel which the water
reaches at axle height – 9 o'clock. If the water strikes at a point below
that, between 8 and 9 o'clock, it is counted a low breast wheel, and
above it, between 9 and 10 o'clock, it is a high breast wheel. The lower
the striking point, the greater the *volume* of water required; the higher
the point, the greater the *fall* of water required.

Since the sixteenth century, breast wheels have been extensively
used. They are reasonably efficient, not as expensive to maintain as
some overshot wheels and less likely to suffer ill-effects in a flood. A
vertical hatch controls the amount of water running on to the wheel,
to make good use of the power available.

Sir William Fairbairn made a number of improvements to the breast wheel as already mentioned on page 46. The basis of his calculations was a peripheral speed of about 4–6 feet per second with a distance between buckets, measured at the periphery, of between 1ft and 1ft 6in. Low breast wheels were designed with buckets slightly further apart than high breast wheels, with the most effective number of buckets, relative to the diameter of a wheel, as shown in the table:

Diameter in feet	No of buckets
10	20–30
20	40–60
30	60–90
40	88–120
50	120–150
60	130–180

The efficiency of breast wheels was generally claimed to be about 55 per cent, but Fairbairn's ventilated buckets improved on this. Loss of water may be reduced by building up the breast or structure supporting the water supply to follow closely the outline of the wheel, but for high breast wheels of 25ft diameter and upwards a close-fitting breast is not essential, since the buckets, having narrower openings, retain the water longer on the wheel. Loss from spilling is usually too small a percentage of the power to justify the expense of a close-fitting breast. If fitted, however, the best breast is one built up in stone rather than iron or wood. It is important to ensure that leaves, twigs, weeds and other floating debris do not pass the sluice to jam between the buckets and the curb at the top of the breast. The damage can be extensive, expensive and most frustrating for the miller.

Pitch-back wheel
This type is not as uncommon as is sometimes suggested, though it is certainly not one of the most common methods. As the name suggests, the wheel is pitched or turned back towards the head race, turning in the same direction as an undershot wheel with spent water in the tail race usually passing under the wheel. Water is brought along a launder the width of the wheel and with well built-up sides. An end-stop prevents water going beyond the centre line of the wheel so that all the water falls out of a slot in the bottom of the launder before the top of the wheel, or 'on the near side', as some millers say. Millers found it worthwhile to go to some trouble to seal the end of the launder so that there was no loss or overshooting of the water causing backwatering of a different kind at the top of the wheel. Buckets face

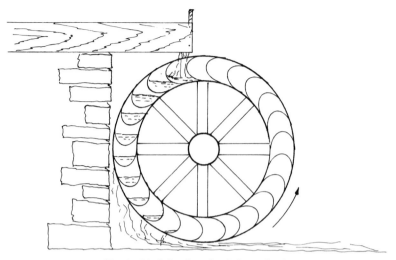

Fig 6   Pitch-back or backshot wheel

the same way as those on breast wheels and therefore there is no risk of backwatering in the usual sense from the tail race, hence one of the reasons for the introduction of this type of wheel in preference to the overshot wheel.

Overshot wheel

This is probably the most efficient wheel, the most attractive and the most noticeable. It is, however, essential to have a site where there is a good fall of water so that a good head can be built up. Considerable

Fig 7   Overshot wheel

10 *left* Pitch-back wheel at Strand Mills, Dawlish

11 Pitch-back wheel, Bridgnorth

earthwork may be necessary to build up the head race from the weir and necessary diversions for flood water. A millpond is also usually built and this is one of its advantages – a larger stock of power in hand. Moreover, the overshot wheel needs only about a quarter of the volume of water required by an undershot wheel since it is using the *weight* of water and not its impulse.

There are some disadvantages apart from the limitation of finding suitable sites with an adequate fall. The overshot wheel has a tendency to a sudden burst of speed if there is a decrease in load, requiring adjustment of the control gate. If there should be a slight trickle of water through a leak in the penstock after the gate has been closed at the end of a day's work, it is possible that there would eventually be a sufficient weight of water in the buckets to turn the wheel. There is a tale that neighbours of one mill used to believe it was haunted because the wheel would occasionally start turning in the middle of the night! The 'ghost' could be kept away by cutting a slot across the trough floor which would normally be plugged or covered in some way, but would be left open at night so that any trickle of water fell on to the back of the wheel and simply rolled over the outside of the buckets. Alternatively, the runner stone could be lowered on to the face of the bedstone so that there was too much resistance to allow the wheel to turn – but some millers decry this as a poor method, claiming it may damage the cutting edges on the stones.

Water begins to fall out of the buckets before they reach the bottom of the wheel, thus reducing power, but careful design of the shape of the buckets can do much to obtain maximum efficiency. When possible, a good miller will run the wheel with the buckets not quite filled to reduce spillage and conserve supplies of water. Twelve cubic feet of water per second should give 1hp for every foot of fall. The Millers', Merchants' and Farmers' Ready Reckoner of 1861 states that if the fall is 1ft, the wheel should turn 2.83 times per minute, and if 20ft, it would turn 12.68 times per minute.

A variation of the overshot wheel, used more in Continental countries, is the alpine wheel.

Alpine wheel

This requires a fast, falling stream, though not necessarily a great volume of water. A channel or trough directs water over the top of the wheel. The difference is that the channel is inclined at an angle of about 30° to the horizontal so that the water strikes the wheel at about 1 o'clock, coming from the left. Both the impulse of the flow and the weight of the water in the buckets are, therefore, involved in turning the wheel, producing relatively high efficiency, but of course the site must be suitable.

To avoid confusion, it should be pointed out that there is also the Alpine horizontal wheel, very similar to the description given on page 62. An excellent example of this has been re-erected in the Museo Nazionale Della Scienza Technica da Vinci in Milan.

Multiple wheels

The practice of using more than one wheel at one site or mill is quite old and much more common than one might imagine. The classic and probably the oldest known example is the flour factory built between AD 308 and 316 by the Romans at Barbegal near Arles in Provence, southern France. Water flowed down a double race from an aqueduct and passed through eight overshot wheels in each race – a total fall of 62ft. Each wheel was coupled to a pair of stones about 3ft 3in in diameter. The factory was capable of producing 28 tons of flour in a ten-hour working day, sufficient to provide for a population of 80,000.

Another outstanding example is the ladder of fourteen wheels rebuilt by Rannequin at Marley on the Seine in 1682 for Louis XIV's palace and water gardens at Versailles. Though nothing of such magnitude exists in Britain, there are several sites where two or three wheels have been used and are still in existence. Nether Alderley Mill in Cheshire has two overshot wheels, but was obviously built so that originally it had a third undershot wheel, probably to drive ancillary equipment. Two fully restored mills in Cumbria – Little Salkeld Mill near Penrith and Eskdale Mill – both have two 12ft diameter overshot wheels in series.

An example of a different kind is provided by the twin wheels at Cheddleton flint mill in Staffordshire. These wheels are not, in the sense of the previous examples, using the same water, but they are arranged opposite one another, one on each bank. Of similar, but not exactly the same size, they are now fully restored and in working order.

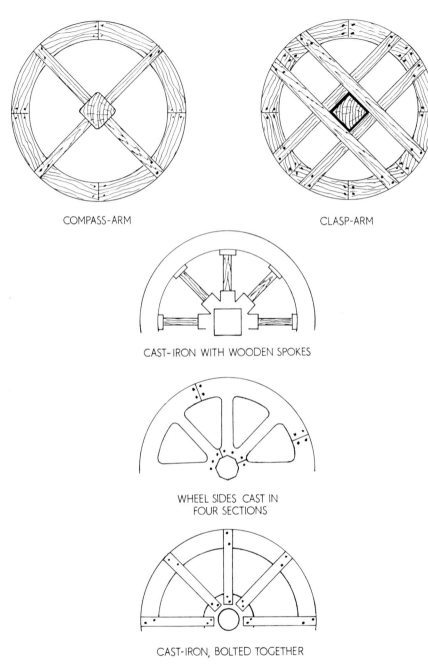

COMPASS-ARM

CLASP-ARM

CAST-IRON WITH WOODEN SPOKES

WHEEL SIDES CAST IN
FOUR SECTIONS

CAST-IRON, BOLTED TOGETHER

Fig 8   Types of wheel construction

WHEEL CONSTRUCTION

The earliest wheels were constructed in timber; although little information is available, models in the Science Museum in South Kensington, London, 'illustrate possible methods used by the Saxons'. No doubt methods used at first followed those of the wheelwright in producing cartwheels. The spokes were fitted into mortises in the axle tree, which was often up to 1ft 6in square. Balance and adjustment of this type was not easy and the number of mortises made the axle a weak spot. They are often referred to as compass-arm wheels. Many millwrights preferred the clasp-arm construction. Spokes crossed the wheel from rim to rim, two pairs on each side, each pair clasping or fitting tight up to the sides of the axle tree. Adjustment of the final position of the wheel could be made by driving wedges on each face of the axle tree. As in wheelwrighting, the rims were made in sections known as felloes. The joints between these would often be strengthened by an iron strap, and then the outer end of the spokes would be fixed to the felloes.

Clasp-arm wheels were not particularly strong, especially where the spokes were wedged to the axle tree. The development of cast iron, notably in Coalbrookdale in Shropshire by Abraham Darby in the early eighteenth century, brought new possibilities for wheel construction. 'Iron-mad' Wilkinson took out a patent there in 1758 for a new method of hollow casting in dry sand using moulding boxes. Smeaton soon adopted this new technique, first for the axle and then for a full wheel. Some iron wheels followed the traditional construction of felloes, spokes and hub bolted together; in others, the spokes of various cross-sections were fixed to a single rim and the hub by means of flaunches. Then, as casting techniques improved, complete sections – usually a quarter of a wheel, consisting of part of the rim, two spokes and part of the centre boss – could be produced and bolted together.

In many instances, wheels were a mixture of wooden and metal construction; in this way the miller obtained a better balanced wheel of reasonably long life without the full expense of an all-metal wheel. Frequently, these composite wheels had a casting fitted round the square axle tree. It would have eight channels in it, each taking a

12 Detail of a cast-iron wheel at Morden Mill, Cornwall

13 Detail of a much older wheel shaft at Cockington, Torquay

wooden spoke; another casting or a metal plate would then be fitted on the outside, encasing the ends of the spokes which were bolted through the castings. The rim castings had sockets in them for the outer ends of the spokes to fit into. Castings frequently have the maker's name and perhaps a date moulded into them – an interesting study on their own!

To complete the wheel, the paddles were normally attached to short wooden or metal posts known as starts, let into the rim of the wheel. Some wheels have bracing rods connecting the starts on each side of the wheel for extra stability. Starts were often set on a radial line but could be placed at different angles depending on the fall and volume of water available at the site. Metal floats were usually attached to starts made with a slight curve. In such cases the metal sheet would be bolted to the start and to the rim of the wheel.

Wheels with buckets have them mounted between deep flat rims, sometimes called shrouds. The wooden boards forming the buckets may fit into grooves cut into wooden rims, or if the rims are cast, into channels or on to flanges in the casting, or they may be bolted to the rims. Metal buckets may be of a variety of shapes and are usually bolted on to flanges on the inside of the rims.

Finally, in some wheels built from the end of the eighteenth century, particularly those used for larger mills such as cotton mills, a toothed rack may be found on the inside of the wheel rim, on the building side of the wheel. This rim gearing meshes with a small pinion wheel mounted on a shaft passing into the mill, and was an alternative method of transmitting the power through the mill. The main advantage of this was to reduce the torque on the wheel shaft. The torque applied by the water is its own weight multiplied by the radius of the wheel. Since waterwheels rotate comparatively slowly, the torque was high in comparison with the power produced. To avoid failure in the shaft due to the shearing action of high torque, wheel shafts had to be of large-diameter material. The rim drive allowed the small pinion to run at high speeds with a much smaller torque on its shaft, while the main axle had simply to support the weight of the wheel.

INSIDE THE MILL:
GEARING AND POWER TRANSMISSION

GEAR CONSTRUCTION

Early gears were made of wood in two parts: the lantern pinion made by setting 'rounds' or 'staves' between two solid discs, and the trundle gear made by setting a row of pegs in a single flange. Usually one or more staves were left loose in the lantern pinion so that they could be removed by being lifted vertically to put the wheel out of gear. The smooth action of this type of gearing was achieved by having a 'hunting cog', an extra peg included in the trundle gear so that each peg did not engage with the same stave in each revolution. A lantern pinion may, for example, have 12 staves and the trundle gear 49 pegs.

Smeaton used the new cast iron for gears as well as shafts, but continued to use lantern pinions and trundle gears. Developments in the mathematical determination of accurate gear teeth came along at about the same time. The use of epicycloidal curves (formed by a small wheel rolling round the outside of a large wheel) and hypocycloidal curves (a small wheel rolling round the inside of a large wheel) for shaping gear teeth was described in 1752 by C.E.L. Camus, Professor of Geometry in Paris, and later by De la Hiré. Leonhard Euler, while Professor of Mathematics in Berlin in 1760, and Göttingen in 1771, both investigated the use of involute curves, but it was not until well into the next century that gear cutting was done by machine. Until then, teeth were 'chipped and trimmed by the good old system of a penny an inch'.

Wooden cogs have never been completely replaced by casting methods. For one thing, when wooden cogs engage with the iron teeth of larger wheels, the amount of noise is reduced considerably; for another, wooden cogs gradually mould themselves individually to the shape of the iron teeth, resulting in a much smoother motion of the whole machinery. A damaged wooden cog is not difficult to replace and a good miller would keep a reserve stock. The wooden cogs were driven up to the shoulder into the mortises in the gear wheel; two wooden wedges could hold them against the dovetail on the shank which projected through the inside of the rim, but a more common

14 A corn mill powered by an undershot wheel, driving a trundle gear and lantern
pinion (E). From *Theatrum Machinarum Novum* by G. A. Böckler, 1662

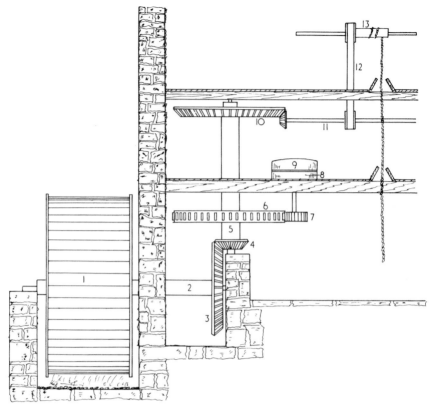

Fig 9 Layout of main gearing, showing one pair of stones; stone furniture omitted. 1 waterwheel; 2 axle tree; 3 pit wheel; 4 wallower; 5 upright shaft; 6 great spur wheel; 7 stone nut; 8 bedstone; 9 runner stone; 10 crown wheel; 11 lay shaft; 12 belt drive; 13 sack hoist

and cheaper method was to drive iron pins through the shanks of the cogs, close to the inside rim of the wheel. A hard, smooth, close-grain hardwood, not prone to splitting, was required. Some millers may have had their own favourite timbers, but apple (or even crabapple), hornbeam, cherry, beech, whitethorn, thorn and acacia can be found, with holly and box as rare possibilities. Oak, ash and elm, all open-grained woods, were used for axle trees, felloes and floats respectively.

FROM WHEEL TO STONES

Inside the mill, mounted on the axle tree carrying the waterwheel, is a large pit wheel, which is usually made of cast iron, though a few wooden ones remain. It runs parallel to the waterwheel and is in a pit called the cog pit. The nearer the pit wheel is to the waterwheel, the greater the reduction in torque on the axle tree. The end of the shaft or

15 The gearing at Bacton Wood Mill, on the old North Walsham and Dilham Canal near North Walsham, Norfolk. The spokes of the waterwheel can be seen in the background, with the pit wheel in front, engaging with the wallower. At the top of the picture is the great spur wheel

axle tree is mounted in a bearing in the brick or stone wall forming the cog pit.

To move the rotation through 90° from a vertical to a horizontal plane, the pit wheel engages with a bevelled pinion, fixed near the bottom of the upright shaft. This is the wallower (sometimes thought to have originated as 'follower'); it is usually of iron with a much smaller number of teeth to make the upright shaft rotate faster than the waterwheel.

The upright shaft is often of wood and is so solid that it gives the impression of carrying the whole mill. Pitchpine and oak are often used in sizes up to 1ft 6in square, carefully chamfered or even shaped to an octagon. Iron ones of round, hexagonal or octagonal sections have been used in more recent mills. The weight of the upright shaft and the gear wheels mounted on it is taken by a thrust bearing, preferably mounted as near as possible above the bearing for the wheel shaft. In some mills this is mounted on a wooden beam but in others, giving easier access, there is a cast-iron arch supporting a bridging box containing a footbrass in which the gudgeon at the foot of the upright shaft can revolve. Four screws in the sides of the bridging box can provide lateral adjustment.

Once when at Tealby Thorpe Mill in Lincolnshire, I was interested to find out what problems a miller had in maintaining the upright shaft in good running order, so I asked the late Percy Richardson. With a slim smile of satisfaction he said: 'A penny a year does it!' By slipping a penny into the bearing at the bottom of the shaft, he provided a bronze bearing surface which took a year to wear down to paper thinness. And that was in the days when a penny was 1d! You may be delayed, chatting to the owner or guide as you look round a mill, but you will be better equipped to understand and appreciate what you see.

Above the wallower on the upright shaft is the great spur wheel, very much larger and sometimes up to 10ft in diameter. The construction may be wheelwright fashion with spokes tenoned into mortises in the upright shaft – the compass-arm method, as used, for example, at Nether Alderley, Cheshire. The clasp-arm method can be found in other mills such as Heron corn mill in Cumbria. Again, oak was used for its strength, but for the vertical gear teeth, the traditional timbers were the fruit woods such as apple or cherry, although beech and hornbeam were quite common.

The great spur wheel engages with very much smaller iron or wooden pinions known as stone nuts, one for each pair of millstones. In remote areas with a limited water supply a mill may have only one pair of stones, but two, three or more pairs were quite common, and

16 The paddle wheel at Felton Mill, Northumbria, on the River Coquet. Top left of the photograph is the stone nut disengaged by a jack ring

some examples of multiple stones still survive. The stone spindle passes through the floor above, through the bedstone and into the runner stone. But this we shall see on the stone floor. The bottom of the spindle is supported on the bridge tree, a wooden beam forming part of the hursting – the framework, usually timber, which supports the millstones.

Some arrangement is necessary to enable a miller to put any stone nut out of mesh, either at the end of the day or for dressing a stone. It is also unlikely that a miller would wish to use all his pairs of stones at the same time; as will be explained later, different stones were used for different purposes. Where the stone spindle carries a conical collar to prevent the stone nut accidentally dropping out of mesh, various methods can be used to lift the stone nut out of gear. A good method frequently used involves supporting the stone nut on a jack ring. This consists of an iron ring from which two rods pass through the bridge tree on either side of the bridge box carrying the toe bearing for the stone spindle. A square-threaded screw passes through a plate connecting the bottom ends of the two rods; a handle attached to the nut can be turned to lift the stone nut out of mesh.

At another mill there may be a lever pivoted on the bridge tree, with a fork at one end under the stone nut. Pressure on the handle at the other end will lift the stone nut out of gear and an adjustable peg in part of the hursting will hold the lever in position. The yoke and chain method is a similar alternative. A chain, attached to a beam above, supports a yoked lever. Two further chains are fixed one to each end of the yoke on either side of the stone spindle, and these are hooked to opposite sides of the stone nut. Pressure on the handle end of the lever will lift the stone nut.

Finally, a more old-fashioned method, still seen sometimes, is the use of slip cogs. By taking out the fixing pegs and removing three or four adjacent cogs, the stone nut would not mesh with the great spur wheel and would therefore stop turning.

UNDERDRIFT OR OVERDRIFT

The method of transmission so far described is known as underdrift. Although by far the most common, there are mills where the drive is from above – overdrift or gripe-driven mills. In these, a long shaft known as a quant or quill (or even a crutch pole) drives the stone. The top of it is held in a glut box – a bearing that can be opened. When the outer section of this is removed, the quant leans out from the great spur wheel and the stone nut is thus disengaged.

Many other variations of gearing and transmission can be found.

THE MILLSTONES

THE STONE FLOOR

Mind those steps on the way up! They may be well worn after years of contact with a miller's footwear. Woodworm may have been there before you as well. There is not much excuse for live woodworm nowadays, but millers in the past had little defence. The grubs do not leave visible evidence of their presence until they have done the damage and it may be your weight on the top softwood step that finally brings about the collapse. Incidentally, there are 'Health and Safety' supporters who may consider that you should wear a hard hat, particularly if exploring a disused mill.

17 The tun encasing the stones and stone furniture at Thorpe Mill, Tealby, Lincolnshire

There may be little to see of the actual millstones. A wooden casing, known in various areas as either a vat, tun or hurstle, leaves access only to the eye at the centre of the runner stone. Standing on the vat is the horse, a timber frame which supports the wooden hopper. Grain, which is stored in bins on the garner or bin floor above, is delivered through spouts into the hopper; it then falls into the shoe or slipper and so into the eye of the runner stone.

The grain gradually passes across the breast of the bedstone to the skirt and then emerges at the circumference. Some mills have a tag or paddle attached to the runner stone which helps to sweep the meal round the space between the edges of the stone and the vat to a hole in the floor, through which it falls down a spout and into the sack below. Just above the sack will be a slot in the top or side of the wooden spout so that the miller can insert a wooden stop when the sack is full and has to be changed.

It is important to ensure that a regular feed of grain to the stones is maintained. Grain tends to hoard in the runner eye; it is equally undesirable for the stones to run 'dry'. The eyes of French burr stones are often fitted with a tin lining, known as the tin eye, to assist in the process, but the all-important item in maintaining a correct feed is the damsel. This is an upright iron shaft [though timber has been used] with a forked end resting on the rynd so that it rotates with the stone. Its upper end is held in position on the beam above. Millers say that it gets its name from the fact that it makes more noise or chatter than anything else in the mill! As it rotates, because of its beaters or shape, it catches usually three or four times in one revolution on a block of hardwood, the 'rap', which is fixed on the inside face of the lower end of the shoe. This agitates the shoe, causing a steady flow of grain to fall into the eye. To ensure that the shoe returns to its correct position, a miller's willow might be used. This is a twig of willow or other springy timber, fixed either to the horse or to the top of the tun at one end, with the other end fixed by a piece of string to the front of the shoe. In other mills, you may find metal springs in use for the same purpose.

Now let us follow how the runner stone is made to rotate with the stone spindle seen on the floor below. The stone spindle passes through the bedstone where it is supported on each side of its journal by tight-fitting brass bearing pads in a square bearing block or neck box. To prevent grain getting into the bearing, a cover or hackle plate is fastened over the neck box. The part of the stone spindle projecting through this is square in section and usually tapered. On the top of the stone spindle rests the rynd, the arched iron bar crossing the diameter of the eye of the runner stone, with its two ends set in lead in the underside of the stone. Again, several variations on this method have been used in different areas and different ages.

THE ALARM

Whilst looking at the stone furniture, as it is sometimes called, there is another item to look for. A good miller would be anxious to make sure that the stones never ran dry. Valuable time could be wasted if, by dry running, the stones lost their cutting edges or were damaged in any other way. There was also the possibility that friction could produce sparks and start a fire. Some form of alarm was therefore necessary, and a common method was to have a leather strap across the hopper above the eye of the stone with a small bell attached to it. When full, the weight of grain would hold down the strap and hold up the bell. Eventually, if left, the strap would be released, shooting upwards and allowing the bell to fall. It would usually fall on to some moving part, frequently the damsel, and warn the miller in no uncertain way.

ROTATIONAL SPEED AND GRINDING CAPACITY

It is the peripheral speed that is important – the speed at the circumference of the stone – and therefore the rotational speed of a stone depends on its diameter. Standard speeds are considered to be: 2ft 6in diameter – 250rpm; 3ft diameter – 200rpm; 3ft 6in diameter – 180rpm; and 4ft diameter – 150rpm.

To determine the waterwheel speed required for a typical mill having 4ft diameter stones running at 150rpm, the calculation might be as follows. A stone nut with 24 cogs would be driven by the great spur wheel having 132 cogs. This would provide a reduction in the ratio of 5½ to 1. Below the great spur wheel, on the same upright shaft, would be the wallower with 36 cogs which would be driven by the pit wheel with 109 cogs; the reduction at this stage would be 3 to 1 (allowing for one hunting cog). Therefore:

$$\text{speed of millstones} \times \begin{array}{c}\text{stone nut to}\\\text{spur wheel}\\\text{reduction}\end{array} \times \begin{array}{c}\text{wallower to}\\\text{pit wheel}\\\text{reduction}\end{array} = \begin{array}{c}\text{waterwheel}\\\text{speed}\end{array}$$

$$150 \times \frac{1}{5.5} \times \frac{1}{3} = 9\text{rpm approx}$$

Only a guide can be given here as to the quantity that can be ground, since much depends on the type and condition of the corn being ground and the purpose for which it is intended. Again, taking

4ft diameter stones as an example, 5 bushels of corn could be ground in one hour, producing nearly 3cwt of flour or nearly 2cwt of fine-dressed flour for breadmaking. If the corn is ground into coarse meal for cattle food, these quantities might be doubled.

TYPES OF STONE

Though little may be seen of the stones in use, it is likely that there will be spare stones leaning against the wall of the stone floor, ready dressed for replacement or awaiting the dresser. The following are the most common stones to be found.

Peak stones
These came mainly from the north-eastern parts of Derbyshire and the south-west of Yorkshire, which are rich in deposits of Millstone Grit. Other areas have been quarried – the red sandstone of Herefordshire, for example, for some early Welsh barley stones. The conglomerate rock formation from Buckinghamshire and the similar stone from Trillek, Gwent, have been used, though Telford referred to the latter as hard and flinty, causing stones to wear smooth and glazed in a short time, which meant more frequent dressing. He also mentioned stones from Anglesey which were grey, soft and gritty but of lasting quality, and an open gritty stone from Mow Cop on the Cheshire–Staffordshire border. But it was from delightful spots such as Froggatt Edge, Curbar Edge, Baslow Edge and especially Stanage Edge, Fox House and Hathersage Moor that the majority of millstones originated. Some of these areas are still littered with complete or partly cut stones left, it would appear, as if to be finished on the next day. But the masons never returned, the quarries were closed and now the stones are nearly overgrown. On a pleasant spring hike across the moors, readers may enjoy a moment's pause sitting on a partly cut stone, trying to imagine how stones of such a size could be moved from such remote places a hundred years ago or more. Peak stones are suitable for grinding cattle grist but have also been used in the past for barley, oats, beans and peas.

French burr stones
Necessary for grinding wheat, these were generally agreed to be the very best obtainable and were found only in the Paris basin at La Ferté-sous-Jouare, seventy kilometres east of Paris, and at Epernon, sixty kilometres west of Paris. The stone is a chalcedonic hornstone or freshwater quartz found among beds of freshwater limestone lying above the chalk. It varies in quality and in colour according to the

amounts of mineral oxides present. Unfortunately, it is no longer quarried and examples are becoming valuable. It had to be quarried in small pieces; these were sorted into grades and then trimmed to fit together – using a similar principle to that of building a stone arch – to form a complete stone of even quality, about 4ft in diameter. The pieces were held together with plaster of Paris, and banded with iron.

Irregularities in the quartz help to maintain a good grinding edge, renewed as the stone wears. French burr stones are therefore more suitable for the finer grades of flour. They have been so much in demand in the past that at one point *The Globe* of 29 September 1809 carried an announcement that they could be imported for three months under special licence, although England and France were at war at the time.

Others

Other stones have been imported. The Dutch blue stones and the 'cullen' stones from Cologne were sometimes used for wheat – though they did not have the grinding power of the French burrs – and a similar kind of lava rock quarried by the Rhine near Andernach and Koblenz was used for a time.

Some mills had artificial or composition stones which were later introductions, consisting of ground particles of stone, sieved and set in a cement. They could have the advantage of even texture, whereas natural stones sometimes have soft spots. Since they were mounted on a cast-iron backing plate, they could be worn down to thinner sizes and were suitable for ancillary equipment in some farm mills. There are examples still to be found.

LIFTING THE RUNNER STONE

The real quality of the miller's products comes from the attention he gives to his stones, and this is one of his first problems. When dressing was required, smaller stones could be moved fairly easily by first inserting one or two broad iron chisels which would make room for wooden wedges, normally with handles and called handspikes. Once the stone was clear of the spindle, a loop in a rope could be passed through the eye. The end of the rope was passed through this loop and then through a hook in the beam above. The weight of the stone was taken by the miller as the edge slipped on to a wooden platform. Some craftsmen could manage this single-handed, but two men would usually be required to pull on the rope while a third man with plenty of weight would lever from the back with the handspikes. The stone would then be rolled over on to a couple of waiting sacks of bran.

18 The gibbet and calipers being used in replacing a runner stone at Wickham Market Mill on the River Deben, Suffolk

Many mills had a number of stepped wedges known as 'many heights', which could ease the task of lifting and lowering safely. A well equipped mill may have more elaborate equipment such as the iron gibbet and calipers, a simple form of crane. The crane arm may be fixed to the floor, and some have a strengthening arm fixed to a beam. A vertical screw passes through the top of the gibbet and at the bottom of the screw, two lugs carry the arms of the calipers. A pin at the bottom of each caliper arm fits into a hole in the edge of the stone. A crossbar on the nut can then be turned to lift the stone clear; once clear, it can be swung away from the bedstone, turned over and lowered for dressing. Other mills used a 'block and falls' or a pulley block and chains. The restored mill at Little Salkeld in Cumbria has a very fine example of a wooden worm drive which turns a long wooden shaft to which ropes are attached for lifting the stone.

STONE DRESSING

Grinding in a mill is fundamentally a scissor-type action, the sharp edge on one stone meeting the sharp edge reversed on the other stone. The first essential of stone dressing, therefore, is to produce those sharp edges. Secondly, the stones must be shaped so that the meal is kept moving freely across the bedstone to leave at the periphery in a fine condition.

To achieve this, the surface of each stone is divided into ten harps as shown in fig 11. Each harp is divided by four furrows, leaving flat surfaces between them known as 'lands'. The furrows taper from nothing at the inside edge to around ½in deep at the outer edge. The 'master' or longest furrows have one edge tangential to the eye of the stone.

The stone dresser first takes out the proof-staff, a steel surface plate about 4ft long and 4in square in section, usually kept very carefully mounted in a wooden case with a hinged lid. This is to test the accuracy of a wooden paint-staff which in turn is used to test the flatness of the grinding surfaces of the stones. When a pair of stones is to be dressed, the miller will first 'prove his staff' by applying a very thin film of oil to the proof-staff and then lightly rubbing the edge of the paint-staff on it. The high spots are thus marked with oil and these can then be removed by scraping with a piece of steel or, very often, a piece of glass.

The paint-staff, a little longer than the diameter of the stone, might be something like 5in by 3in in section and shaped handrail-fashion along the top edge. Various timbers such as red deal, oak, mahogany or walnut are known to be used for the purpose; the very best ones are considered to be those made of timber sawn into three thicknesses, the outer pieces being reversed and rejointed with glue and brass screws. Those in one piece should have the annual rings as near horizontal as possible to avoid warping or twisting.

After proving the paint-staff, the next process is the staffing or facing of the stones, also known in some parts as flawing. The face of each stone is rubbed with burr – a small piece of burr stone with a prepared flat surface on one side – to avoid scratching the staff more than

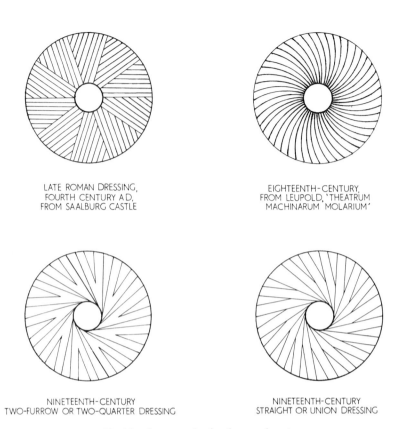

LATE ROMAN DRESSING,
FOURTH CENTURY A.D.,
FROM SAALBURG CASTLE

EIGHTEENTH-CENTURY,
FROM LEUPOLD, 'THEATRUM
MACHINARUM 'MOLARIUM'

NINETEENTH-CENTURY
TWO-FURROW OR TWO-QUARTER DRESSING

NINETEENTH-CENTURY
STRAIGHT OR UNION DRESSING

Fig 10   Some methods of stone dressing

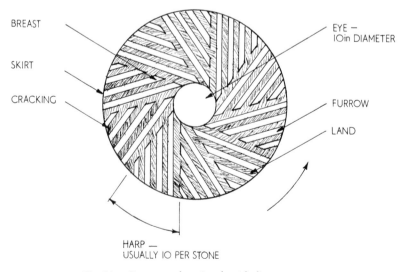

BREAST

SKIRT

CRACKING

EYE —
10in DIAMETER

FURROW

LAND

HARP —
USUALLY 10 PER STONE

Fig 11   Common dressing for 4ft diameter stones

19 Staffing the stone at Saxlingham Thorpe Mills on the River Tas, Norfolk

necessary. Then the staff is coated with raddle, a mixture of red-oxide and water known occasionally as 'tiver'. Two brushes are required: first a wet one to apply the raddle and then a dry one to remove any surplus. When rubbed over the stone, the staff will mark the high spots with raddle and they can then be chipped away.

The next stage is furrowing or drifting. To mark out a new stone or to check existing ones, two furrowing strips are used. One is made the width of the furrow (about 1⅛in for the average-sized stone) and one the width of the land (about 1¼in). These are very simple but very useful tools, made in red deal and about ⅜in thick. More up-to-date mills may have metal stencils for the purpose. The deeper edge of the furrow is cut first with a pick leaving a simple groove as in plate 21, then the slope from the land to this depth is chiselled out with a mill-bill. Mill-bills are best made from high-carbon steel and when new are about 11in long and 1½in square in the middle, drawn down to a chisel point at each end, with the cutting edge ground to 40°. They weigh 3–3½lb when new; this reduces with frequent regrinding, and when down to about 2lb they are considered too light for use.

20 Mill-bills and thrifts by the millstones at Thorpe Mill, Tealby, Lincolnshire

The mill-bills and picks are fixed in wooden holders known as the thrifts or hefts. These are usually beautifully made, and frequently become highly polished after hours of use in the hands of the miller. Ash is perhaps the timber most used for this purpose, but chestnut and beech thrifts can also be found.

The final process in dressing a stone – and probably the one needing most skill – is cracking or scratching. This consists of cutting a number of fine cracks or grooves on the lands with a fine pick. For this, the miller divides the stone into three parts: the skirt – one third of the radius at the outside; the breast – the central third of the radius; and the eye – the third nearest the centre of the stone.

A good dresser was said to be able to 'crack sixteen to the inch at the skirt', making the cracks lighter to die out at the middle of the breast, but stones are often found with only twelve or fourteen cracks to the inch. These fine grooves are sometimes known as 'harp strings'. An inexperienced dresser would either tap too gently and have to strike more times, taking longer to complete the dressing, or else he would strike too hard and inaccurately, making a poor job. The dresser would sit on the skirt of the stone with his left elbow resting on a 'bist' – a small bag of bran made up for the purpose – and would move round the stone until it was completed. A well equipped mill might have a turntable for stone-dressing and, though these are rare, there are still some to be seen.

21 The late Mr Edward Rackham, of Messrs E. R. and R. T. Rackham Ltd, stone-dressing at Wickham Market Mill, Suffolk

The direction of the grooves appears to be the same on both stones as they lie for dressing, with the runner stones reversed. When the stones are in position, of course, the sharp edges will meet each other like a pair of scissors. Peak stones were usually dressed clockwise, but French burrs were dressed widdershins (against the sun). French stones took much longer to dress than Peak stones. But so much depends on how often the stones are dressed.

The interval between stone dressing depends on a number of factors. The blend of corn used would have a marked effect, some types of wheat, for example, being much harder than others. One of the reasons why dressing becomes necessary, it should be remembered, is because the sharp edges of the stone become 'built up' with a coating of meal and this has to be removed to reveal the stone again. Inevitably, some stone is removed each time as well, and a stone will eventually be reduced to about 3in thick before it is relegated to the doorstep. French burrs will probably need dressing after a good 300 hours' grinding, when over 2,000 sacks of corn have passed between them. A lazy miller will only find that the stones take longer to dress.

Nowadays, of course, anyone wishing to keep a mill in working order may have to be prepared to develop the skill of stone dressing himself. But there was a time when dressing was considered a trade in its own right, and there would be itinerant craftsmen, the 'tramping millers', who would call at a mill asking for 'a couple o' days work'. If the dresser was unknown, he would be asked by the miller to 'show his metal'. Judging by the minute black particles embedded in his skin, the miller would assess how experienced the caller was at stone dressing. Sometimes dressers worked in pairs, in which case the senior man usually took the runner stone.

REMOUNTING THE RUNNER STONE

Skilful dressing was important for good milling, but it was equally necessary to ensure that the runner stone was mounted correctly so that an even gap between the stones was maintained throughout a complete revolution. Two essential requirements had to be attended to before remounting: one was to 'pack the neck', which ensured that no dust could enter the bedstones's neck and throw it off balance, and the other was 'brigging the spindle'. Since the stone spindle supports and turns the runner stone, it had to be in the correct position before remounting could begin. The old method of brigging involved driving wooden wedges down the sides of the spindle bearing. To check that the bedstone was level, millers used a gable, a triangular frame with a lead weight or plumb-bob hanging from its apex. The point of the weight should coincide with a centre mark on the base of the frame when set on the stone. To check that the stone spindle ran true, most millers had some form of trammel or jack stick, consisting usually of a wooden arm with a square hole at one end to fit over the spindle. A feather or small brush attached to the other end in such a way that its height could be adjusted would check that contact was made with the stone throughout the complete revolution. The miller would set the wheel turning at a slow pace, probably sprinkle a little flour on the stone, and then any unswept parts would clearly indicate in which direction adjustment of the spindle was required.

An improved method of adjustment was introduced in the nineteenth century using the bridging box. This is a cast-iron box with a hackle screw on each side. The foot of the spindle rests on a pad in the box and by adjusting the pressure on the four screws, the position of the spindle can be adjusted until vertical.

When a new runner stone was to be mounted, it would have two 3in square holes cut out about halfway down the skirt, diametrically opposite one another, to take the pins for the lifting tackle; at the same time, small pockets were sometimes chopped out of the back of the stone so that molten lead could be poured in to balance it once remounted. A much improved method – the balance box – was patented by Henry Clarke in 1859. This was made in cast iron and was let into the top of the runner stone. It contained lead weights on a screw adjustable in the vertical plane, while the mass of the weights could be lessened by removing some of the lead. Thus the stone could be

22 Pair of French stones with the inscription 'This stone worked the first time March 28th 1859', at Otterton Mill, Budleigh Salterton, Devon. The balance box can be seen on the right

balanced both in the vertical and horizontal planes. Once mounted and true there remained one vital operation before grinding could commence – tentering.

TENTERING

Apart from the speed of the stones, the rate at which the grain is fed to the stones and the condition of the grain, the vital factor governing the fineness of the flour or meal is the gap between the stones. It is the adjustment of this gap that is known as tentering. The gap is always small, but its actual size depends on the method of milling. In England, the common method is known as 'low milling' the stones are kept close together and in the same position all the time. But on the Continent – especially in Hungary, using harder grain – the stones are brought closer together in stages so that the grain is broken down more easily; this method is known as 'high milling'.

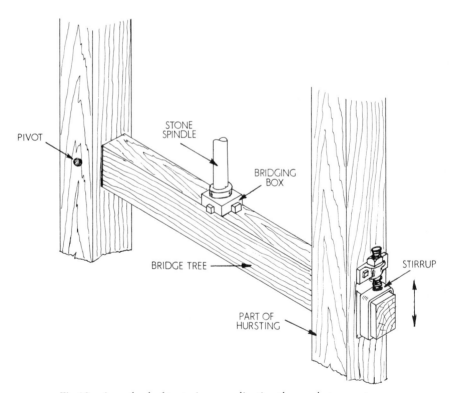

Fig 12   A method of tentering, or adjusting the gap between stones

23 Inside Worthing Mill on the River Wensum, Norfolk, showing the governor

Methods of tentering vary considerably and are sometimes rather crude since the gap is adjusted in such a way as to alter the angle of the stone spindle and put it slightly out of true, making a further fine adjustment of the stones necessary. As already described, the stone spindle, passing through the centre of the stones, rests in a footstep bearing on a timber beam known as the bridge tree which forms part of the hursting or framework supporting the stones. In a common method of tentering, the bridge tree is pivoted in the hursting at one end and has the other end tenoned into an upright called the brayer. The oversized mortise in this allows the bridge tree a little movement up and down. The end of the bridge tree is held in a stirrup from which a square-threaded rod projects upwards, through a bracket mounted on the brayer, and is held in position by a nut. Adjustment of this nut will lift or lower the stirrup and, therefore, the bridge tree, providing a very fine adjustment of the gap between the stones. Alternatively, the bridge tree can be fixed and the bridging box mounted in a vertical slide in it. A peg supporting the box is fixed centrally on a lever below the bridge tree, pivoted at one end and attached to a screw at the other. By means of a bevel gear, the screw can be turned by a handwheel on the outside of the hursting, to raise or lower the bridging box and stone spindle.

If tentering is carried out when the stones are cold, a check should be made when they have been running for about half an hour. In mills where the supply of water can be relied upon to maintain a constant speed, no further tentering should be necessary. Elsewhere, if the flow of water to the wheel cannot be adjusted to maintain a steady speed then adjustment of the gap between the stones ought to be made to compensate for any alteration in speed. Automatic tentering has been used in some mills by means of a centrifugal ball governor, a method used in windmills since 1787. The faster the shaft of the governor rotates, the further out the balls fly. These are linked to a sliding collar at the bottom of the shaft, which will rise, taking with it a rod connected to a tentering device, and therefore adjusting the gap between the stones.

THE CROWN WHEEL

The upright shaft coming up through the stone floor is held in the top journal bearing on the side of the beam above. Mounted near the top of the shaft is the crown wheel. It can hardly be missed – it is frequently at about eye-level, and its construction may be similar to that of the great spur wheel, either clasp-arm or compass-arm construction. The crown wheel engages with another, much smaller, bevel gear and thus transforms the movement to turn a horizontal lay shaft. This provides the miller with power for a variety of additional pieces of equipment which sometimes include quite ingenious devices of his own invention.

SACK HOIST

The most common use of the lay shaft is to drive the sack hoist. As grain arrives at a mill, it is usually taken up to the garner or bin floor at the top. The hoist is therefore invaluable. Its rope or chain passes through the centre of a double trapdoor in each floor; these drop down to a closed position as soon as the sack has passed through. Some mills may be fortunate in having a lucam, a small, often timber-covered platform projecting from the top floor over the entrance to the mill. There is sometimes a small window, or even just a small hole cut in the boarding of the side of the lucam, to provide a lookout for the miller waiting for an incoming delivery of grain. The lucam contains an external sack hoist so that sacks of grain can be lifted directly off a vehicle in the yard or roadway below without having to be taken inside the mill. In other mills, sacks would have to be taken inside by sackbarrow to a point below the hoist.

A variety of methods of operating the hoist can be found. Frequently the slack and tight belt principle is used. From a pulley wheel on the lay shaft, a belt drive takes the power on to a pulley – usually wooden and of wheelwright construction – mounted on a beam above. Attached to the top pulley is a winding drum which is supported by a fixed bearing at one end. At the other end, the flanged pulley wheel is held in a bearing which can be moved vertically. When not in use, the winding drum will drop a little at this end and so slacken the belt. A

24 The bin floor at Holton Mill on the Holton Brook near Wheatley, Oxford

gentle tug on the control rope will operate levers to lift the bearing, tighten the belt and set the hoist in motion. Other gadgets, such as those for preventing the sack going too high, or for operating the trap-doors, may also be found.

ADDITIONAL MACHINERY

Cleaning the grain
The removal of impurities from the grain, which is perhaps one of the first essentials, could be done by either a vibrating action or a rotary movement. Sieves, made of woven metal or perforated sheets, separated the larger impurities or 'overtails' from the suitable grain which was known as 'throughs'. The simple reel separator, mounted with a slight slope, was rotated by a belt drive from a lay shaft. Grain fed in at the top passed over different meshes which allowed small impurities to pass through, then the grain further down, leaving the larger over-tails to pass out of the end of the reel.

Another method of separation, relying on the weight of impurities, was used in the aspirator. This used a fan to draw air through a column of grain as it was fed into a spout. The lighter impurities such as pieces of chaff and dust were blown out. A good aspirator machine would pass the grain through several stages of separation. Later

25 Interior showing sack hoists at Letheringsett Mill on the River Glaven, Norfolk

machines that combined both the reel separator and the air-draught principles were very effective, but the late nineteenth and early twentieth centuries produced a number of improved ideas.

A French invention of 1845 separated by means of shape. The trieur had a rotating cylinder, again canted but with a corrugated inside surface. Inside the cylinder was a fixed conveyor box. The impurities and round grain of unwanted cereals were held in the recesses of the cylinder and carried upwards until they fell into the conveyor box, then carried by a rotating screw into a separate container. The wheat was carried along the bottom of the cylinder by gravity and through a spout into a waiting receptacle. The disc separator which appeared later was an improvement on this basic method.

Another machine, the smutter, was used to remove dirt and any diseased particles attached to the grain, replacing scouring methods. A series of metal beaters rotating inside a cylinder of wire mesh caused the grain to rub against the mesh, thus removing the dirt. The grain would then be passed through an aspirator to remove the dust.

Flour dressing
The meal that resulted from grinding the grain contained particles of bran. These could be removed by sieving but instead of metal, some form of fine cloth or silk was used. The wire machine or dresser was,

yet again, a canted cylinder lined with sifting materials, the finest at the top. The cylinder and its lining were fixed, but inside, a series of revolving brushes pushed the meal against the mesh until it fell through into selecting hoppers below. The brushes revolved at quite a fast speed – between 300 and 500rpm. The first hoppers received the 'top' grades of flour. Lower hoppers would take the 'middlings', leaving the bran to travel right through the machine to fall into a separate hopper. The whole machine was usually built inside a large wooden case.

Bolters were an early form of bran separator, consisting of a long cloth sleeve which was inclined so that the top of it received the meal as it left the stones. A wooden rod, agitated by the stone drive, shook the flour through the sleeve, leaving the bran to be collected below.

Towards the end of the nineteenth century, equipment for refining became much more sophisticated, particularly in the larger mills where centrifugal reel separators were installed. These made use of more of the sieving area. The reel and silk rotated at about 20rpm; beaters revolved inside, in the same direction but at up to 2,000rpm. These machines required more power, of course, but since the rotating reels lifted the meal so that it fell on to the beaters, it was forced at the inside surface of the sieve, increasing the rate of production.

For a small mill such machinery was expensive, consumed excessive amounts of power and required more space than was often available. In such circumstances a plansifter, using a flat sieve with reciprocating motion, was employed. Full details of this kind of machinery, which was made about the end of the nineteenth century, can be obtained from old catalogues of makers such as W. Gardner of Gloucester.

Miscellaneous
One often finds other pieces of equipment in the mill, most probably on the stone floor, particularly if it is a farm mill or at least one which has had to become a grist mill to continue in existence. Rollers for crushing oats or flaking maize were quite common and so were bean kibblers, chaff cutters and machines for breaking up linseed cattle-cake. Vertical 'stone' grinders using a manufactured material such as carborundum were introduced in time for some mills to install them.

Finally, a mill may have some supplementary power such as a steam or gas engine. Some farm mills, only using the machinery for cattle food, might have used the power take-off on a tractor or have installed an oil engine using a flat belt drive. Eventually, when electricity supplies became available, electric motors were installed. Alternatively, the complete reverse might be found: a dynamo to produce electricity, thus giving the waterwheel new life.

THE MILLER'S PRODUCTS

When, in the nineteenth century, the Continental millers developed the great roller mills and the reducing process which started the craving for white flour, they claimed it had better keeping qualities and produced a tall, well piled loaf. This was true, but they did not realise that they were extracting the small but important part of the grain that provides essential vitamins. How could they? It was not until 1912 that Dr Funk isolated a factor he called *Vitamine*, which could cure beriberi. Two further factors were discovered in 1915 and the identification of vitamins has continued to develop since then. Would flour milling have taken a different course if these two major developments had been made in reverse?

A grain of wheat consists of three main parts: the endosperm – 84 per cent; the bran – 14 per cent; and the germ – 2 per cent. The endosperm is divided into compartments by lines of cellulose, each compartment tightly packed with starch-filled cells. Modern roller mills split the grain of wheat by rapidly revolving 'break' rolls, releasing the endosperm without crushing the outer layers of bran. It is then sieved by plansifters and purifiers to separate the bran and the germ from the endosperm, which at this stage is called semolina. This is then passed through smooth rolls, known as 'reduction' rolls, to produce the flour – a white flour referred to as 70 per cent extraction of the original grain. One grain of wheat produces about 20,000 particles of flour.

The bran consists of several layers of protective covering, a layer of colouring matter which indicates the variety of wheat such as red and white, and the aleurone layer containing cerealin. These are used for animal food and 'All Bran', for example. The cerealin tends to soften a dough and make rising more difficult.

The third, smallest and yet perhaps the most important part of the wheat grain is the germ, but it spoils the colour of the flour, so out it has to go. There is, admittedly, another reason: the germ contains fat which tends to go rancid. But the germ also contains vitamins of the B group – thiamine, nicotinic acid and riboflavin. These liberate energy from glucose and are essential for growth and general good health. The body does not usually manufacture its own vitamins; a diet of protein, carbohydrate, fat, minerals and water is not sufficient. It has therefore become a legal requirement that all flours must contain not less than 1.65mg iron, 0.24mg thiamine and 1.60mg niacin per hundred grams of flour. Although these additives replace the vitamins and minerals extracted by modern milling, the flour does not have the roughage that, by encouraging peristalsis, helps the digestion process to take a shorter time, thus producing a more healthy body.

But all these qualities are in the flour if it is 100 per cent wholewheat flour, produced from the whole wheat grain. Fortunately there are mills, water and wind, still in production or fully restored to production, where one can see and obtain stone-ground flour with nothing extracted, nothing added, and which some prefer to the wholewheat flour produced by roller mills.

An intermediate quality between the wholewheat and the white flour is achieved by returning the wheat germ. To prevent its fat content causing the flour to turn rancid, the germ is cooked, giving it a malted flavour. A mixture of one part cooked germ and three parts white flour is used to produce a brown flour such as Hovis.

Apart from extraction, another factor affecting the resultant flour is the miller's blend of wheat. Some would claim that English wheat has been good enough for making bread in the past and could therefore continue to be so. It is the weak or soft type of wheat because of the climate, and is excellent for making biscuits and cake, but because its gluten content is lower than that of imported wheat, it will produce a loaf of denser consistency. Modern millers, therefore, produce flour from a blend of English and North American wheat, the latter being hard or strong by comparison. The Manitoba wheat, for example, is a very strong red wheat and the Hard Winter wheat of mid-USA is fairly strong.

The condition of the wheat must be correct for the best flour. When harvested, wheat is usually too damp – between 18 and 24 per cent moisture content; this has to be reduced to a level of between 12 and 14 per cent.

Part Three

Watermills Today

26 Former glory retained at the Mill and Mill House, Farningham, Kent

INTRODUCTION:
NEW LIFE FOR WATERWHEELS

Fortunately the number of mills in a preserved or restored state that the public can visit has increased in recent years. Whilst it is regrettable that there is no complete record of watermill sites – as in Holland, for example – some extraordinary efforts are being made by enthusiasts to compile lists and to preserve and restore where possible.

The Society for the Protection of Ancient Buildings, founded in 1877 by William Morris to 'protect our ancient buildings and hand them down instructive and venerable to those that come after us', has for fifty years had a windmill and watermill section, providing support for preservation, encouragement to millers and many publications about mills. Supporting and supplementing that work are various local mill groups and local historical and archaeological societies. The growth of interest in industrial archaeology has encouraged more restoration to take place. County planning departments have taken greater interest and carried out commendable restoration programmes in several areas. The Stratford corn mill at West Harptree, a mill site from before Domesday until 1952, might have disappeared in the bed of the Chew Valley Reservoir, but it was dismantled and re-erected in the grounds of Blaise Castle House Folk Museum. Whereas Part One of this book ended with a note of sadness, recording how mills have come to the end of their lives and been lost for ever, certain of the developments mentioned towards the end of Part Two have meant that other mills have gained a new lease of life and can still be seen today – 'instructive and venerable' for this and future generations.

Adding to the encouragement to preserve mills in a productive capacity are those who question the effects of chemicals in the production and preparation of our foodstuffs. At Little Salkeld Mill in Cumbria, for example, it is claimed that organic farming – combining the old system of crop rotation with the returning to the land of manure and organic matter – ensures a high degree of natural fertility in the soil and a corresponding health, strength and resistance to disease in the crops. No artificial fertilisers or toxic chemical weedkillers are used, producing a quality reflected in the nutritional value and flavour of the wheat. The whole wheat germ can then be used – essential if the best food value is to be achieved.

Finally, we are living in an age in which it is steadily being realised that the consumption of the world's energy resources cannot continue at the present rate much longer. Moreover, if we have any thought for future generations, it is time we began to consider methods of energy conservation. 'Alternative technology' has therefore emerged, and some thought has been given to the use of water power again. Water is a natural source of power and a sensible society makes good use of it. The search for a means of breaking the first law of thermodynamics, that energy cannot be created out of nothing – a perpetual motion machine – has gone on for centuries. The Abbé de la Rogue produced one in 1686, but overlooked the fact that the pressure at a given depth below a water surface is constant and does not depend on the surface area of water. This and many other attempts have been based on a waterwheel, but the answer has yet to be found.

THE SOUTH AND SOUTH-EAST

Take the A20 out of London and this will enable you to see the very picturesque sight of Farningham Mill in Kent, not so far from Lullingstone Castle. The view of the neat lawns and the water disappearing under the mill with its clean-looking weatherboarding crowned by the lucam and mansard roof is not to be missed.

The road leads on to Maidstone, and nine miles further on is Chegworth Mill in Harrietsham. It is not so long since its overshot wheel drove three pairs of stones, but at the time of writing it is in need of repair. Whilst in this area, any water-power enthusiast must surely wish to visit Faversham. Chilham Mill, near Chilham Castle, could be included on the route; it is a tall, five-storey building with a vast amount of weatherboarding and a well-designed lucam to the top floor.

Faversham has been a great centre for water power. The history of its gunpowder factories goes back to the reign of Queen Elizabeth I, and it is believed that had Guy Fawkes succeeded in his plot, the Houses of Parliament would have been blown up by Faversham gunpowder. There have been numerous mills here in the past and as long ago as 1760 they were nationalised and became the Royal Powder Mills. They played a prominent part in the Napoleonic and Crimean wars, but eventually it became obvious that their position would be too vulnerable in an international conflict. Through a series of mergers, the remaining works became part of ICI and work ceased in 1934. Now the valiant efforts of the Faversham Society have admirably restored the remains of Chart Mill, which may be viewed by appointment. One of two breastshot wheels, 16ft in diameter, remains; the drive is taken through the usual wallower mounted on a vertical shaft. A second shaft of timber is driven by spur gearing and this in turn drives two millstones which are mounted on horizontal axles as edge runners for grinding the gunpowder.

From Faversham, the A2 leads into Canterbury and through Dover, the next 'port of call'. A detour along the A257 will allow a call to be made at Wickhambreaux Mill on the River Nailbourne, four or five miles from Canterbury. This is a large, six-storey, weatherboarded mill which has an interesting small wheelhouse with a curved roof.

Though it may be more interesting to take the road through Deal, it will be more direct along the A256 from Sandwich to Crabble Mill, two miles north of Dover. Here another organisation, the Cleary Foundation, is to be congratulated on its efforts in preserving more of our island's heritage. It is a large mill, similar in size to Wickhambreaux, with an external paddle wheel and a good example of a governor inside for controlling its speed. On the third and fourth floors are good examples for those looking for flour-grading machines: a shaker grader and a smutter. In the nineteenth century, the mill supplied much of its output to London's growing population; it ceased work in 1890. Now Dover Corporation has accepted responsibility for its maintenance so that it can be opened to visitors on Bank Holidays and during the summer.

From Dover, take the A20 to Ashford. Some five miles or so before reaching Ashford is Evegate Mill in Smeeth. Unfortunately, this is not in working condition, but there is no doubt that S. G. Child & Son would be glad to show any visitors round their antiques showroom and their cabinetmaking and upholstery workshops at the mill.

Not far away, on the other side of the main road to Ashford, is Swanton Mill in Mersham. This mill is in a highly commendable condition thanks to the efforts of Gay Christensen. Restoration has been going on since 1969, and in 1975 the work received a Civic Trust Award during European Architectural Heritage Year. The East Stour river powers an overshot wheel which is a little uncommon in that its diameter is less than its width. The mill once had a beam engine to provide supplementary power but this is now in the Ford Museum, USA. Mrs Christensen encourages school visits to the mill; in fact, local children have contributed to the mill's activities. It is possible to obtain wholemeal flour and to sample home-made scones in the tea room. At the right time of year, visitors can see the mill's own Maris Widgeon wheat being harvested with a binder.

Now take the A28 from Ashford towards Hastings and you may catch a glimpse of Worten Mill in Great Chart, only just out of Ashford. This is a beautiful house, standing on what is thought to be one of the oldest mill sites in the county. The earliest remaining record is that of King Ethelbert II confirming in AD762 a deed whereby the monastery of St Peter and St Paul transferred half the produce of the mill to the Royal Mill of Wyth (now Wye).

Just through Rolvenden, turn right along the A268 and then left on to the A265 towards Heathfield. Half a mile south of Burwash is Bateman's, the great home of Rudyard Kipling. Built by a local ironmaster in 1634, it was Kipling's home until 1936. At the bottom of the peaceful garden is the watermill about which Kipling wrote:

> See yon our little mill that clacks
>   so busy by the brook?
> She has ground her corn and paid her tax
>   ever since Domesday Book.

Two springs, from Pook's Hill and from Nether Forge, supply water to the millpond and then the overshot wheel, but in 1903, Kipling installed a turbine by Gilbert Gilkes and Co of Kendal to provide electricity for Bateman's. Now owned by the National Trust, the mill has been skilfully restored, yet another project to receive a Civic Trust Award in European Architectural Heritage Year. Both turbine and waterwheel now work and once again stone-ground flour may be purchased by visitors when the mill is open, between March and September.

Another detour might be made to Michelham Priory watermill, near Upper Dicker; this is a good example of the monastic mills mentioned earlier. Also in the area are the mill in Cross-in-Hand and Moat Hill Mill in Mayfield, but the outstanding mill, not to be missed, is Haxted Mill at Edenbridge on the River Eden, just on the Surrey–Kent border. This is another mill with a very long history. It ground wheat for flour until 1918 but continued to provide grist for local farmers until 1944. Mr C. E. Woodrow has since spent twenty years working on its restoration and collecting milling exhibits before opening

27 Haxted Mill at Edenbridge, on the Surrey-Kent border

Haxted in 1969 as a most interesting watermill museum. His knowledge and enthusiasm for the subject make a visit well worthwhile; the mill is open on Saturdays, Sundays and Bank Holidays between Easter and September. The wheel standing outside is a showpiece rescued from a Cornish tin mine. The mill's own wheel is overshot, made of cast iron, but has new fibreglass buckets.

Not so far from Gatwick Airport is Ifield Mill near Crawley, which has been restored by the Sussex Industrial Archaeology Society and was opened to the public in 1979. Originally it was the site of a forge, but the present mill was built on the site in 1817. It has not worked since 1927 and further work has yet to be done before working demonstrations can be given. To the south-east is Horsted Keynes Mill, a small weatherboarded mill, and just north of Haywards Heath is Dean's Mill in Lindfield, Sussex. Since 1970, it has been privately owned by Mr W. M. Rowe in conjunction with a chain of health food stores. A neat-looking weatherboarded mill, it busily produces whole-wheat flour for its customers.

Now take the A272 from Haywards Heath to Cowfold. Just to the north is Suffold hammer pond, which used to supply one of the old furnaces in the area; now its sluices appear to be beyond repair. The A281 from Cowfold leads to Woods Mill on Shoreham Road in Henfield. This has been owned by the Sussex Trust for Nature Conservation since 1966; its wheel dates back to 1854 and still turns sometimes. The mill has been restored and can be visited most afternoons.

An alternative route from Cowfold is to take the A281 across to Rudgwick in Sussex, within a short distance of the Surrey border, to see Gibbons Mill. This used to be a corn mill driven by an undershot wheel, but in 1901 it began to be used for generating electricity. A Francis turbine was installed in 1930 to continue this work, with the help of a diesel engine from 1946. In about 1960, mains electricity put the mill into retirement, though it is still used occasionally.

Just to the north of Worthing is Ship Mill in High Salvington. Also in the area is the Weald and Downland Open Air Museum at Singleton, north of Chichester, with its reconstructed seventeenth-century watermill from Lurgashall to the north. Then there is the water-powered beam pump at Coultershaw Bridge near Petworth, another of the Sussex Industrial Archaeology Society's projects. About halfway to Petersfield to the west and still in Sussex is Terwick Mill near Midhurst on the River Rother, which worked as a grist mill until 1966. Part of the building is stone with the upper storey timber-framed with weatherboard cladding; this dates from 1600, but a larger, more sturdy building was added about 1750.

Cross the boundary now into Hampshire to see one of the most pic-turesque mills with ducks on the four-acre pond and colourful creeper covering the wall. This is Headley Mill near Bordon, about eight miles north of Petersfield. J. Ellis & Sons (Bordon) Ltd are still very actively producing their own special wholewheat flour. They use all English wheat, grown on their own farm or within a twenty-mile radius of the mill. The water is from a tributary of the River Wey and turns a breast-shot wheel 12ft 6in in diameter and 7ft 6in wide. The mill has four pairs of stones, three of them French burr, and the wheel is able to drive two pairs at a time since the water supply is quite reliable and stable, even during a dry summer. The mill was filmed by the BBC in 1970.

THE ISLE OF WIGHT

According to the Domesday Book, there were twenty-four mills on the island. The three most notable watermills still surviving are all towards the south-west corner. Not far from Shorwell on the B3399 is Yafford Mill, part of a farm park and open to the public. It has been principally a grist mill and worked as such until 1965. For a further five years Mr Salter, the last miller, continued to work the mill a few days each week. The overshot wheel is not a common design, being a wooden wheel with iron buckets. Instead of the usual launder, water is carried from the millpond along an iron pipe which is supported by a wooden frame. In addition to stones, the mill has a roller crusher. Other interesting features include a wire machine and a worm screw which fed seven sacks through canvas sleeves, thus allowing the mill to run with minimum attention for a considerable time.

Lower Calbourne Mill deserves a mention here, though it has been driven by an Armfield turbine since 1890. It ceased work in about 1962, but was resurrected by John Pretty and his wife who make an unusual miller/ballet teacher combination. The mill has been active again since 1973 using water power mainly for dough mixing; how-ever, the flow of water is not plentiful, so a Ruston and Hornsby oil engine drives one pair of stones and an electric motor the other pair, producing 'Miller's Damsel' wholemeal flour from 2½ tons of island-grown wheat per week.

About a mile to the south is Upper Calbourne roller mill, Mylplace, Calbourne, which is a much larger mill in a very attractive setting. The Weeks family have operated the mill since 1878 and when, in 1955, it became uneconomical to run, they decided to retain everything in working order and develop a rural life museum. The overshot wheel still produces cattle feed when required, and operates regularly for its summer visitors. It has been calculated that since the wheel turns at about six times a minute and has forty-eight buckets, it needs 225 gallons of water to produce 1lb of meal.

RETURN TO THE MAINLAND

The first call might be Beaulieu tide mill; it was once worked by a wooden undershot wheel, and two pairs of stones are supported by an iron hursting, which replaced an earlier frame towards the end of the nineteenth century.

Christchurch is of interest to anyone in search of watermill history. Place Mill, also known as Prior's Mill, is near the Quay where the River Avon and River Stour join; it has been a boat shed for most of this century. Throop Mill worked as a corn mill until 1974, though it has been powered by an oil engine and has not used water for some time, but the remains of a wheel still exist. There have also been two other mills – Borough Mill and Knapp Mill – in the area, but little remains of them.

Between Southampton and Portsmouth are the remains of Titchfield Mill with its two iron breastshot wheels side by side. A few miles to the north is a well-known mill – Chesapeake Mill in Wickham. This is a four-storey brick building with a dormer-type timbered lucam built out from the roof; its most interesting feature is that the beams used in its construction were taken from the American frigate *Chesapeake* after it had been captured by HMS *Shannon* off the coast of Boston in 1813. To the north-west of Southampton is Nursling Mill. Built into its brick wall is a stone tablet with the inscription:

This Building Stands on
A Frame of Large Beech Timber
which was given by Sir Richard Mill, Bart
in memory of whose kindness this
Stone was placed here by
T.C.K. 1728

A detour might be made to West Harnham Mill just south-west of Salisbury. This is now a pottery with quite a decorative external appearance, and water still flows under the building. The main venue, however, must be Winchester.

The importance of Winchester as an old-established centre for the use of waterpower has already been mentioned on page 21. It was the capital of Wessex and became a central market place for Hampshire's grain and wool. It was also provided with natural power in the form

of the fast-flowing River Itchen. By 959 there were three or four mills in Winchester, and it is possible that the highest number working at one time rose to twelve. City Mill was built as a tannery in about 1743, though some parts are of an earlier date – probably removed for use from an older building. It worked as a corn mill for over a hundred years, but was faced with probable demolition in 1928. Fortunately, by local enthusiasm, funds were raised to purchase the mill and present it to the National Trust. Since 1931, it has been used by the Youth Hostels Association. It has a waterwheel but the machinery has been removed.

Winchester also has the attractive working Abbey Mill, and Durngate Mill, at one time used for grinding and fulling simultaneously. In its latter days, Durngate Mill has been powered by an Armfield turbine driving two pairs of stones supported by an iron hursting. North-east of Winchester on the River Alre is an old fulling mill now converted into a very attractive house under which the water still flows. With its dormer windows peeping out from the thatched roof which caps its timber frame and white-painted panels, it presents a vastly different scene today from that which it must have known in its sixteenth-century fulling days.

The A34 leads north towards Newbury and passes through Whitchurch. This journey will provide an example of the wide variety of architectural interest to be found in a quest for watermills – from the thatch of Alresford Mill to the impressive Georgian building of Whitchurch silk mill. A three-storey building crowned by an ornate cupola, its central pediment frames a clock erected to celebrate victory at Waterloo. It was originally a wool-spinning mill, but changed to silk, and until the 1950s was powered by a low breast wheel which had a Fairbairn-type clutch control hatch. Electricity has now replaced the wheel for producing its high-quality silk. No doubt its workforce is somewhat different from that of 1838, when 39 of its 108 employees were under the age of thirteen.

Further north, leaving the A34 to cross towards Kingsclere, is Ecchinswell Mill with two pairs of stones. Its upright shaft, with its many sides making it almost round, seems an ideal design to fit its surroundings. Across country, to the north-east of Basingstoke, is the mill in Sherfield-on-Loddon – timber-framed with brick infill. Presenting a completely different picture is Elstead Mill, Surrey, a few miles beyond Farnham to the south-east; it is now a house of five storeys, capped by a weather vane on a dome supported by six columns.

(*opposite*) 28 The beautiful West Harnham Mill near Salisbury, Wiltshire

About 1½ miles south of Guildford is Shalford Mill, a timber-
framed building which the National Trust has cared for since 1932,
though it has not worked since 1914. Its low breast wheel and machinery can be seen in their restored state. Part of the mill, Watermill Cottages, has been converted into a residence for the custodian.

The area just north of Guildford can in itself provide a tour of mills,
all receiving their water from the River Wey and its tributaries. Stoke
Mill, by Guildford, ground corn until 1957, using a turbine in its
latter days. Just to the north at Burpham is Bower's Mill, now converted into a handsome residence with few remains of any mill workings.
Then, where the Stamford and Hodge brooks meet in Pirbright, there
is a gathering of mills. Rickford's Mill between Worplesdon and Pirbright, and Pirbright Mill itself, have been converted into residences.
Heath Mill is also a residence but still has its overshot wheel which is
dated 1832. North-east of Woking is Pyrford Mill and not too far
away was Newark Mill, sadly destroyed by fire in 1965. Still further
on, in the same direction, is Byfleet Mill which is on a private estate; it
is a weatherboarded building that stands next to the charming mill
house owned by Robert Bolt, the playwright, who has carefully
restored the mill. Two or three miles along the A245 is Cobham Mill
on the River Mole – an early nineteenth-century corn mill which has
been leased by the Surrey County Council for restoration. A little to
the south on the other side of the A3 is Ockham Mill, also a private
residence. Then last, but by far not the least, is the large Coxes Lock
Mill at New Haw. It had a very wide waterwheel until a turbine was
installed in 1894. Towards Dorking, about five miles from Guildford,
is Gomshall Mill, now an antiques showroom and restaurant. It
ceased work as a corn mill in about 1960, but most of its machinery
and its wheel have been restored.

To complete the tour of mills in the south and south-east, a working
mill with a restaurant could be quite appropriate. Seven miles east of
Redhill is Coltsford Mill in Hurstgreen, Oxted. It has been in the
Heasman family's care since 1860. Animal feed is still being produced
by Mr W. Heasman, while his son runs the restaurant.

THE SOUTH-WEST

To begin a tour of this area in Bristol should not be difficult to justify as Bristol owes much to the use of water power in the past. The Baptist Mills, the home of brass-foundry work, once had nine undershot wheels to provide all the power. Then there was Ashley Down Mill, now part of the water board's property, and travelling towards Bath there were Saltford Mill, Shawford Mill, Kelston brass mill and Claverton where John Rennie converted a mill with a 20ft diameter breastshot wheel into a pumping station for the Kennet and Avon Canal. Bath has lost most of its evidence of water power, and just to the south, Twerton has lost the double mill – one mill on each side of the weir – that it had for centuries.

A first call might, however, be made at the Blaise Castle House Folk Museum just north of Bristol, where the Stratford Mill at West Harptree, carefully dismantled when the Chew Valley Reservoir was constructed, has been rebuilt. Now its breastshot wheel and the internal machinery are working again.

A 'must' to visit is the Priston Mill off the A367 just south of Bath, which is now restored and in full production of stone-ground wholewheat flour. The site's history goes back to Anglo-Saxon charters and the Domesday Book. Now it has an enclosed pitch-back wheel, 21ft in diameter and 4ft wide, installed in about 1850. The mill is part of a large farm and its water supply comes from the Conygre Brook, though it appears to have had a leat connecting it to an additional reserve supply at some time.

The journey from Bath to Warminster may well be broken to make a short detour along the B3098 to Great Cheverell Mill in Wiltshire. Valiant efforts are being made to return this mill to an active life. It was recorded in 1449 as a corn mill, in 1526 as a fulling mill, and in the nineteenth century as an 'iron mill' making edge tools; between 1827 and 1880 it was used for making sheep bells! Though most of the machinery is intact, the breastshot wheel was broken up by the water board in the winter of 1963 during a severe frost. The owners are working on the conversion of part of the premises to private accommodation and restoration of the other part so that the mill can operate and be open to the public, exhibiting milling paraphernalia.

Now to continue the journey, the A350 through Warminster leads to Shaftesbury. Just to the south are Cann Mills, outstanding perhaps because of the Portuguese-type windmill, built on the top of the water-mill in 1971. The watermill was burnt down in 1955 but was rebuilt in the following year and is worked every day, all day, by N. R. Stoate & Sons Ltd, to produce wholemeal flour. Water is taken from the River Sturkel, which rises about a mile upstream, and is stored in a 1½ acre millpond. The iron overshot wheel, 9ft in diameter and 5ft 3in wide, was made by E. S. Hindley of Bourton, Dorset in 1874.

The journey across the county is through Thomas Hardy country to Sturminster Newton, once a centre for water-powered woollen mills. An alternative route lies along the A350 and A31 to pass through Tolpuddle, undoubtedly well known for its martyrs of 1834, but also interesting for its thatched roofs and its mill with tiled mansard roof. Just inside Somerset are Clapton Mills in Crewkerne, fully commercial mills producing, among other products, very good stone-ground flour. There are three pairs of stones which run against the sun and a roller mill; the latter provides three breaks and three reductions. A new axle was fitted to the waterwheel in 1937, and since then a new shaft has been fitted to the pinion drive. The great spur wheel has had new iron spokes and, in 1978, a new pinion wheel complete with a new set of cast-iron teeth was fitted to the waterwheel. Thus it is well maintained and has a most interesting history which is well documented. Since the turn of the century it has been owned by the Lockyer family, and Mr Graham Lockyer now continues the tradition.

It is not far along the A30, taking the A358 in Chard, to Hornsbury Mill – an attractive mill which has been open to the public since 1973. It has an 18ft diameter overshot wheel which can be connected to a generator and produce about 2kW of electricity. The River Isle can provide a flow of about 1,500 gallons of water per minute which, with buckets holding 20 gallons each, turns the wheel at about 4–6rpm. Though not in production, the mill is complete, and of particular note is the auger with twenty-eight galvanised iron chutes under which sacks can be suspended for automatic filling. The ground meal could be passed from the second or third pair of stones down to the floor below and into an elevator, which brought it back up, tipped it into the auger and hence into the sacks. This is a fairly modern addition to the mill and once set up, allowed it to operate unattended for several hours. The sack hoist, driven from a lay shaft and controlled by a rope operating a jockey pulley, is also a good example. To round off a visit, there are tempting cream teas available during the summer.

Through Honiton, down to Sidmouth and along the coast is Otterton Mill near Budleigh Salterton. Of particular interest here are the twin wheels, one a low breast wheel and one a Poncelet type. Sluices can direct water to either wheel even though they are side by side. There are three pairs of stones, the French burrs being fitted with Clarke and Dunham patent balance boxes. The runner stones are beautifully inscribed with the dates on which they were first worked – 1859 and 1862. The mill is owned by Clinton Devon Estates and is open to the public during the summer.

An alternative route or additional tour can be taken to Bickleigh Mill, which is on the A396 between Tiverton and Exeter. Originally the site had two wheels, but it now has one undershot wheel; much of its machinery has been taken from Dulverton in Somerset where the Town Mills were dismantled. Thus the derelict Bickleigh Mill has become a hive of industry as a craft centre. The wheel drives machinery for some of the craftsmen who can be seen at work; these include a wood turner and a glass engraver. There are corn dollies, jewellery and flower craft to see, and, if that is not sufficient, observation beehives and an indoor aviary!

From Bickleigh, it is not difficult to make a detour to see Stockleigh Mill, one of the few still thatched. The main route, however, follows the A30 out of Exeter, branching off to the left on the B3212 to find Dunsford Mill. Though this is not a working mill, it is an indication of the extent of edge-tool manufacture by waterwheel power in the past. Powered by the River Teign, the wheel used to operate two tilt-hammers.

A little further on is North Bovey, which once had several watermills. When last seen, one of them, Manor Mill, had roses growing over the wheel. Another was once a woollen mill. A call could then be made at Widecombe-in-the-Moor. There is not a great deal left, but it once had three mills: Jordan Mill, now converted to a home, Ponsworthy Mill, which once had two wheels in line, and Cockingford Mill, which is now a farm guest-house. An alternative for a night's stay is the Mill End Hotel in Chagford, which used to be the Sandy Park corn mill. Chagford has had several mills, including pioneers in generating electricity.

Though little is left, some may like to investigate the remains of a gunpowder mill at Lydford, Postbridge, an isolated spot chosen for safety reasons and for its plentiful water supply. When dynamite was invented, the mill declined and ceased work before the beginning of this century.

In Bovey Tracey there is a large mill building now owned by Standard Telephones and Cables. From here, several other sites could be investigated, such as the mill near the sea front at Dawlish or the old forge, now a gift shop, in Cockington. The main road goes through

Ashburton, once quite a centre for woollen mills and corn mills. In this area, fulling mills are known as 'tucking mills', and this name appears at Rew Mill. Further along the A38 is Buckfastleigh, which had at least five mills in the past. Two of them have been used to generate electricity and one has been a CWS woollen mill for some time. Ivybridge provides an example of yet another application of the power of a waterwheel – paper mills – powered here by the River Erme, though Stowford Mill long ago used a turbine. Cornwood is another possible call as it once had three mills: two for corn and one a sawmill.

Now, bypassing Plymouth, take the A386 to Tavistock. A call could be made in Walkhampton where the wheelwright's shop and Huckworthy Mill used to have waterwheels. But a whole day could be spent if a call were to be made at Morwellham on the River Tamar. Among the many exhibits of this indoor and outdoor museum are three waterwheels. The most attractive to many is bound to be the 32ft diameter overshot wheel. It has, in fact, been removed from a Dartmoor china-clay works, but is on the site where a wheel used to grind manganese. The second wheel is also overshot and was used for pumping water to cottages, and the third one, among farm buildings, originally powered a threshing mill and was driven from the Tavistock Canal.

Not far away is Cotehele Mill in St Dominick. This is part of the Cotehele House estate which it once served and is now owned by the National Trust. It was worked, mainly for cattle feed in its latter days, until 1964, and has also been used to generate electricity. Since 1974, after full restoration, it has been open to the public. It has an external overshot wheel which drives two pairs of stones. There are other buildings to be seen, including a blacksmith's forge and cider press as well as the house itself, making a visit well worthwhile. Still in the Saltash area, there are the remains of Cornwall's last tide mill, long since out of action. Water from an 8½ acre pond used to pass through its four wooden wheels, each about 12ft in diameter.

On the way down to St Austell, only a few miles from West Looe, is the Lanreath Mill and Museum. Unfortunately it has no wheel and the machinery has been taken from another mill, but there are some interesting exhibits such as farm implements and stationary engines. Near St Austell, in Charlestown, is another example of the water powered forges which were much used in this area. At Wheal Martyn, a Cornish lift-beam pump used to be powered by a 25ft diameter overshot wheel. It would pump up clay in the form of slurry which was deposited in settling tanks and then moved into drying kilns. St Austell has made good use of waterpower in the past: the old corn mill

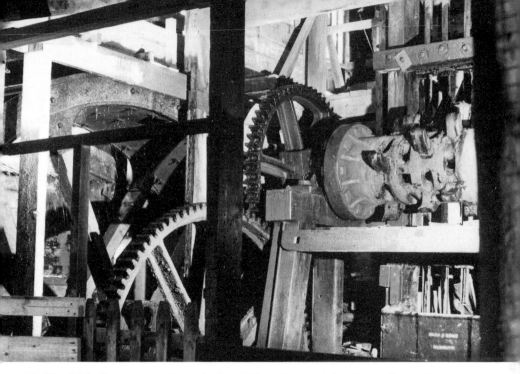

29 The 16 ft diameter overshot wheel at Tolgus tin mine that drives the twelve-headed Cornish stamps – vertical wooden beams shod with iron which fall to crush the ore in the box below

is now a tyre store and the blowing houses have been used at various times for candle making, corn grinding and smelting.

Probably the most southerly working mill in Britain is Roskennals Mill in Newbridge, between Penzance and St Just. Its overshot wheel drives roller plant as well as stones. It ceased working commercially in 1969, but has since been preserved and maintained by its owner, John Charlton. If you wish to explore even further south, there is the Alsia Mill at St Buryan.

The first calls on the homeward journey might be New Mills and then Zennor Mill on the coast road between St Just and St Ives. Zennor Mill has not worked since 1900 and has given up its wheel for the repair of New Mills. Then join the A30 and take the road to Redruth where, in Portreath Road, the Tolgus tin-streaming mill can be seen. Tin mining, of course, has been a major industry in Cornwall, and the waterwheel has played no small part in that work. A 30ft diameter overshot wheel drives the fan for a main furnace to smelt iron and a 15ft wheel is used for other machinery. This tin-streaming mill has been owned by Madame Tussaud's since 1976; guided tours are now provided for the public.

Travelling north along the A39, an interesting detour might be made to see what remains of another of Cornwall's twelve tide mills –

30 Paper making at Wookey Hole, Wells, Somerset – probably the largest hand-made paper mill in the world. The waterwheel has been used to drive wooden stampers which pound the cloth and water from which the paper is made into a pulp known as 'stuff'. In this photograph, the vatman (right) is shaking the deckle to obtain an even thickness of stuff; the coucher (left) then lays the wet sheets between felts (foreground) which are put into the press to remove excess water before being taken to the drying lofts

Sea Mills at St Issey. There was once a 30ft diameter wheel driving six pairs of stones, but that was a long time ago! A little further along, near Wadebridge, is Hingham Mill, Egoshayle, one of the last to work in Cornwall, with a 20ft diameter undershot paddle wheel.

Quite a long journey must now be taken, probably along the A30, to Okehampton. For a small town, it has made good use of its water power, but the more interesting site is the Finch Brothers' foundry in Sticklepath, four miles away. Powered by the River Taw, it began as a corn mill and a woollen mill; in the nineteenth century, it developed as a very active foundry producing agricultural edge tools, shovels and ladles for the china-clay industry. It was worked by three water-wheels. The first turned fans to give the draught to the hearths; the second powered trip-hammers and drop-hammers; and the third turned the grindstone for the final edge-grinding.

The long journey up to the north of the county will be worthwhile because there are two working mills in Ilfracombe. Hele Mill is on the main coast road by a bathing beach, and has many interesting features. During the height of the summer there is enough water to turn the wheel, but there is also a 1927 horizontal National diesel engine for alternative power. Additional items inside include a smutter, a sifter, an elevator, a Wegmann porcelain roller mill, an 18in vertical Blackstone stone mill, a 30in Dreadnought vertical stone mill, a Bamford combined plate and roller mill, a wire machine and a purifier. To add to all that, Mr Lovell, the owner, has bags of wholemeal flour on sale.

Also in Ilfracombe is Bicclescombe Mill, now completely restored by the local Rotary Club and open to the public. It has only one pair of stones, but a large wheel that can produce up to 7hp. The water comes down the Score Valley, along the River Wilder, and joins the sea at Wildersmouth beach.

The final stage of the journey is through Bridgwater and Glastonbury to Wells. Two miles beyond is the paper mill at Wookey Hole, a most interesting part of the Madame Tussaud's Wookey Hole caves, where hand-made paper can be seen in production. Waterwheels, a steam engine and a Donkin water turbine have powered the mill at different times. It is situated at the head of the River Axe which, from where it rises in the Mendip Hills, percolates through the rocks into a sizeable reservoir, falling 40ft. Thus not only is there an adequate supply of water power, but the water is also of the necessary degree of purity for making paper. This and the many other exhibits and attractions make Wookey Hole a very popular place to visit, particularly for a family outing.

NORTH-WEST OF LONDON

Three miles south of St Albans is Moor Mill in Frogmore, which has two wheels and four pairs of stones. It worked until the 1940s and, though complete, is not being used at present. On the River Ver, in the village of St Michaels and near the remains of the Roman city of Verulamium, is Kingsbury Mill, a very smart and well preserved mill, now largely a museum. It ground the grain grown on the Gorhambury estate until the 1920s; Whitworth Bros then used it until 1936. It continued to grind animal feed for some years, then, in 1970, the estates company began the restoration work which is now enjoyed by a large number of visitors.

St Albans has made great use of its water supplies. In addition to those mentioned already, there have been the Abbey silk mills, Shafford Mill and Sopwell Mill, which is now a private house. North-east of St Albans, the A414 leads to Hatfield. Mill Green Mill is the last of Hatfield's four mills to survive with anything of interest to show. It is owned by the Hatfield District Council and is leased to the Hatfield and District Archaeological Society, who are engaged in considerable restoration work. The wheel is undershot with a breast-high sluice gate. Unfortunately, only part of the very old wheel remains, but its construction – oak arms, halved into an oak rim stiffened by iron strapping – is interesting. The original paddles have been replaced by iron buckets.

For short detours in the area, Hertingfordbury has a nineteenth-century mill which was working until 1933, and Wheathampstead had several mills. Batford Mill has little original detail left, but Bridge Mill and East Hyde Mill have more of interest.

There are several possible routes now across country to Ford End Mill, Ivinghoe, three miles from Tring and not far from Whipsnade Zoo. One route may be through Great Gaddesden to see what remains of Noke Mill. Ford End Mill is quite small but has its overshot wheel and machinery in order, thanks to the Pitstone Historical Society and the owners, who ceased to work the mill in the 1950s.

Now take the B489 and the A5120 to Bedford. Three miles to the north-west is Bromham Mill, which belongs to Bedfordshire County Council. They are engaged in an extensive programme which includes restoration of the mill and the development of the associated 6 acre site as a Regional Country Life, Craft and Countryside Visitor Centre. Return to Bedford and cross to the A1 by the A603. A few miles to the south, in Biggleswade, are Holme Mills, which have been in production there since 1855 when there were over 400 mills in the county! The River Ivel still provides power for the original wheel for W. Jordan & Sons Ltd, whose well recommended range of products include Country Bran, Crunchy Toasted Oats, National Wheatgerm, Wholewheat Flour and Country Cookbook Flour.

The return journey may be made through Hitchin which has had at least five mills in the past. Unfortunately, they seem to have been rather prone to fire damage and little of interest remains except perhaps at Charlton Mill.

THAMES AND COTSWOLDS

Travelling north from Oxford along the A34, a first call should be made at Combe Mill on the Blenheim estate, Woodstock, for which it was the maintenance workshop. It originally had a breastshot wheel, but a steam-driven beam engine has been added at the other end of the building, geared to the same system. After years of disuse, restoration began in 1972 by the Combe Mill Society, who give demonstrations from time to time, using the steam engine.

To the north-west, near Ditchley Park, was Coldron Mill in Spelsbury. This had an overshot wheel and was on a site which had been in use since Domesday. The whole of the interior was dismantled and re-erected in the Science Museum, South Kensington, in 1938. Further north along the B4022 and A361, and then some seven miles to the west of Banbury, is Epwell Mill, which is privately owned but may be visited on special days when it is open to the public as part of the National Gardens Scheme. Also near Banbury, Hook Norton Brewery has been water-powered.

The B4035 to Chipping Campden may provide an opportunity to see another attractive scene and support the good causes of the National Gardens Scheme. Westington Mill is privately owned, but when it is opened to the public, the picture presented by the eight waterfalls in the mill stream is a delight to see. The mill last worked as a corn mill in 1937. A few miles south, in Blockley, is yet another picturesque setting where the large stone-built mill has been converted into a private dwelling.

From Blockley, a very pleasant detour may be made by taking the A44 to Broadway, one of the prettiest villages in England, and then the A46 and A438 to Tewkesbury. There are, incidentally, several very interesting ports of call in the area – Snowshill Manor and Buckland Rectory for example – and the visit to Tewkesbury is another opportunity to enjoy a meal in a mill! The Abbey Mill there has been a restaurant for many years and, according to *John Halifax, Gentleman* by Dinah Mulock, was Abel Fletcher's mill. Though it has lost both its wheels, the building is interesting because of its large lucam-type extension over the water from all but the ground floor.

The return journey to the Cotswolds may be along the A38 and A4019 to Cheltenham and then the A40, A436 and B4068. In Lower

31 Abbey Mill, Tewkesbury, Gloucestershire

32 The breastshot wheel at Lower Slaughter, Gloucestershire

33 Arlington Mill at Bibury, Gloucestershire, now a Cotswold Country Museum

Slaughter, the mill is still part of a bakery and the breastshot wheel is used for dough making. There is also a mill in Bourton-on-the-Water, and a little to the north-east is Kingham Mill, four miles from Chipping Norton – yet another good point to call for a lunch. A glass screen has been erected in the restaurant so that customers may see the wheel as they eat. Near Stow-on-the-Wold, Arkell's Donnington Brewery had a corn mill driven by a breastshot wheel.

From the Cotswold area, take the Fosse Way (A429) to Cirencester. Much could be written about the use of the waterwheel in the area just to the south of the Cotswolds. Rock Mill, King's Mill, Eddell's Mill and Cap Mill, all in the Painswick area, are just a few examples demonstrating the importance of cloth mills to the region. Minchinhampton, Nailsworth and Wotton-under-Edge have similar histories and could each make interesting detours in themselves.

Seven miles from Cirencester, on the A433, is the beautiful village of Bibury. Arlington Mill was known to William Morris and has now become, under its present owner, author David Verey, a Cotswold Country Museum which includes a William Morris room. When the mill ceased to work in 1914, much of the equipment was destroyed. It is fortunate, however, that it has become the means of preserving machinery from North Cerney Mill, and although it has no waterwheel, it can be worked electrically. It is a most attractive setting for a fine collection of exhibits, as well as for demonstrating a mill at work.

Now take a cross-country route to Lechlade. Just to the north, along the A361, is Little Faringdon Mill, which was worked commercially until the 1960s. It remained disused for several years until it was taken over by Mr J. R. Taylor who began an ambitious programme of restoration, including the establishment of a trout farm with water from the River Leach. With the help of Harold Lock, the last miller to work there, the mill is being restored so that it can grind corn again.

From Lechlade, follow the A417 through Faringdon, then turn left on to the B4508. This leads into the valley of the River Ock, a tributary of the Thames, which was a prolific supplier of water power to mills. Many are lost and just two are mentioned here. Charney Bassett Mill is in the process of being restored by Oxfordshire County Council. Unfortunately, the breastshot wheel was lost during the last war, but most of the machinery was left intact. Eventually it will be a site museum. The other is Venn Mill in Garford, which has not worked since 1939 but is complete with its breastshot wheel and is in the process of being restored.

The A338 runs into Wantage where Clark's Mill, having a roller plant, still works but is no longer driven by water power. Now turn left on to the A417. There are two calls to make here, the first being at the old watermill in Ardington where Nigel Griffiths uses the premises to make his furniture, all hand-made to high standards in solid oak. The wheel, 11ft 6in in diameter, has its sides cast in one piece with wooden buckets. A little further along is the place to buy some pottery to stand on the oak sideboard found at Ardington. For Pauline Thompson, East Hendred Mill makes an ideal pottery and a beautiful studio. The mill has an undershot wheel and the drives are all wood-to-wood. A few miles to the east is East Hagbourne Mill, a fine mill capable of driving three pairs of stones. It is brick at ground-floor level with weatherboarding above, and straddles the brook.

Travelling down to Newbury, we approach the valley of the River Kennet and then the Thames, with a host of possible sites to investigate. Six miles south-west of Newbury is New Mill in Inkpen. Little remains, but the beautiful garden is open under the National Gardens Scheme; it contains an overshot wheel, built in 1930 to generate electricity. To the east of Newbury is Camberhouse Mill, Thatcham, and just off the A4 to Reading is Tyle Mill, Sulhamstead. Tyle Mill was a corn mill until 1917 and also generated electricity until 1936 when it became a private house; the garden is open under the above scheme.

Turning north along the A340 leads to the Thames and such mills as Goring, Cleeve and the picturesque Whitchurch and Mapledurham.

34 Hambleden Mill, on the River Thames between Henley and Marlow

The latter is in working order and has undergone considerable restoration. The undershot wheel is unusual in its width in relation to diameter. Marks on the mill door indicate several floods. Further down the river is the large Sonning Mill, with a modern roller plant having a wheel and turbines. Between Henley and Marlow is Hambleden Mill, which ceased regular work in 1958 but has since been extensively restored.

Now on to High Wycombe where there have been many mills on the River Wye. Pann Mill, on the open space known as The Rye, has been demolished but the undershot wheel remains and can be clearly seen from the A40. Bassetsbury Mill has been saved after a varied history, including a period as the Chequers Inn and as an antiques showroom. Now it has been converted into dwellings with the wheel preserved and water flowing beneath it. Finally, to the north, beyond Princes Risborough, is Scotsgrove Mill in Haddenham, though it is not easy to find. It was working until 1967.

EAST ANGLIA

Starting from the London area, a tour through the low-lying areas of Essex may not sound promising to those in search of watermills. It is windmill country; but in the past, much power was derived from the county's labyrinth of tidal creeks. The first journey could be along the A127 to Rochford; a mill is mentioned here in the Domesday Book. The building was damaged by fire in 1965 after being used for some years as a store. There was also a tide mill at nearby Little Stambridge, but this had to be demolished, also following a fire.

The A130 runs through Chelmsford and a few miles to the north is the weatherboarded Croxton's Mill at Little Waltham. There is a much larger mill at Coggeshall to the north-east, on Stane Street, now the A120 between Braintree and Colchester. About a mile south of Colchester is Bourne Ponds Mill, probably more attractive architecturally than most mills. Its gable ends – stepped and scrolled, with pinnacles added for good measure – are quite unusual and ornate. The explanation may be that the building was probably intended as a fishing lodge when built by Sir Thomas Lucas in 1591. For many years it was a woollen mill, becoming a corn mill in the nineteenth century. A story is told that the last miller removed two bodies from the pond in one night – an occupational hazard for a miller. It was given to the National Trust in 1936 and its 26ft diameter internal overshot wheel has been restored so that it will turn again.

As the route crosses the border into Suffolk, the number of watermill sites becomes greater and the possibilities of making short tours of the area considerable. First, one could explore the Colne Valley. Near Halstead on the A604 is Maplestead Mill, a large white-painted weatherboarded mill which almost fits the description of Hardwick Hall in Derbyshire – 'more glass than wall'. The present building is thought to be eighteenth-century. It has been a corn mill, converted to turbine power a long time ago, but a large part of the mill is now private accommodation.

Further along the A131, the River Stour becomes the source of power, and there have been several watermills around Sudbury. Sudbury itself has a modernised mill, and a little to the east Great Cornard Mill, which had two wheels, has also been modernised. To

35 Flatford Mill, Suffolk, the family home of the artist John Constable

the north is the nineteenth-century mill at Glemsford, and from there the A134 leads into Bury St Edmunds. So prolific are the mill sites in this area that I must leave the reader the freedom to investigate such places as Cavenham, and Campsea Ash on the River Deben: here the mill with its three pairs of stones ceased work in 1961, but luckily it has been preserved. Icklingham is a modern mill with a turbine, whilst nearby Barton Mills, once having two wheels, have, I believe, completely disappeared. On the Thetford side, several mills have ceased to work – Euston, Fornham St Martin and Ixworth – but Pakenham Mill is being restored to working order by the Suffolk Preservation Trust.

Returning to the River Stour area, there is the one mill that hardly anyone can have failed to discover: Flatford Mill near East Bergholt. John Constable's father was the miller there, and Constable's painting of the mill has become one of the best known of the period. Certainly he was well able to portray the peace and serenity of the mill scene with which he was so familiar. He claimed to be happy only when 'surrounded by weirs, backwaters, nets and willows, with a smell of weeds, flowing water and flour in my nostrils'. Flatford Mill is now owned by the National Trust and used for field study courses. It is, therefore, not open to the public, and in any case all machinery has been removed.

Nearby is Thorrington Street Mill on the River Box, and Layham and Raydon Mills on the River Brett; the latter has had a turbine installed. The Brett has provided power for many mills in the past – Aldham Mill, Nedging Mill in Bildeston, Kersey Mill in Cosford Bridge and Cobbolds Mill in Monks Eleigh, for example. But perhaps one of the most prolific rivers for mill power in Suffolk has been the River Gipping, which is well worth exploring between Ipswich and Stowmarket. The outstanding mill is Baylham, which has a very neat, double-storey lucam projecting from the white-painted weatherboarding and the tiled roof. Needham Market had two mills, Coddenham Road Mill and Hawkes Mill, but neither has worked for some years.

Move on through Ipswich and along the A12 to what might now be considered the highlight of East Anglian mills – the tide mill on the River Deben at Woodbridge. The restoration of this mill can only be described as extensive and exemplary. The mill ceased to work in 1956, by which time repairs were becoming overdue. Deterioration accelerated and the mill was near to collapse when it was purchased by Mrs R. T. Gardner in 1968 and restoration began. It has been open to the public since 1973, and in 1976 a new 18ft diameter clasp-arm wheel with fifty-six elm floats was installed, the main machinery having been restored by Jameson Marshall Ltd of Hollesley. In the

36 Baylham Mill on the River Gipping, Suffolk. Note the unusual two-storey lucam

37 Stoke Holy Cross Mill, on the River Tas, Norfolk, where Colman's mustard was made in the nineteenth century

past, the mill has worked four pairs of stones, and during its latter years it was supported by a diesel engine. The millpond, now a yacht harbour, covered about 7½ acres, storing tidal water and allowing it to drive the wheel with the outgoing tide.

Further north along the Deben there have been mill sites in Ufford and Letheringham. Between them is Wickham Market Mill, which is still capable of turning three pairs of stones. It has an excellent example of the iron gibbet and calipers used for lifting a runner stone (plate 18). The stone being dressed in plate 21 is also at Wickham Market Mill.

Norfolk can offer the watermill archaeologist a lifetime's interest; it has ample supplies of water and is a corn-growing area. A few miles south of Norwich, is one mill of particular interest – Stoke Holy Cross Mill. It was here that Jeremiah Colman made his famous mustard between 1814 and 1856, after which he moved to Carrow. The mill worked, producing animal feed, until 1962, since when it has been converted into a restaurant. Also in the area are Lakenham Mill and Keswick Mill on the River Yare. Further out, on the River Waveney, is Ellingham Mill; once worked by Vitovis Ltd, it is a large building and a hotchpotch of heights, but nevertheless attractive with stone, brick and timber-boarding. On the River Bure, Horstead Mill in Coltishall was a large building with an attractive arrangement of pointed gables and rounded arches overlooking the millpond. Sadly, it was badly damaged by fire in 1967.

38 Keswick Mill on the River Yare, Norfolk

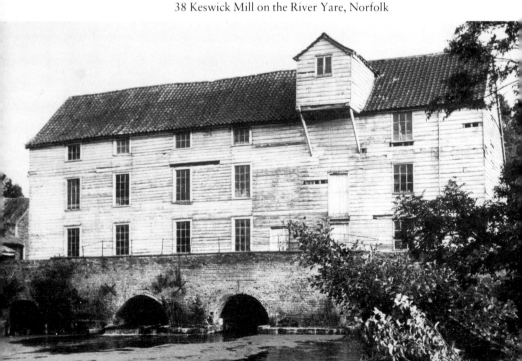

39 The working mill at Burgh-next-Aylsham on the River Bure, Norfolk

40 Weighing a sack of flour at Burgh-next-Aylsham

41 Corpusty Mill on the River Bure, Norfolk

The next call, along the B1354 towards Aylsham, is the large working mill at Burgh-next-Aylsham on the River Bure. This mill has six pointed gable ends piercing the skyline above its horizontal lines of weatherboarding. It is operated by Michael Grix, who can be seen in plate 40. The pattern, however, is different at Corpusty Mill, also on the River Bure, along the B1354 north-west of Aylsham. Here the top floor has dormer windows and a timber-boarded lucam overhangs the end of the building.

An outing to the coast will provide an opportunity for the family to enjoy the sands of Cromer and also see what remains of the old water-powered sawmill at Gunton Park. From Cromer, take the A148 through Holt to Letheringsett Mill on the River Glaven. Plate 25 is a view of the bin floor at this mill, showing the sack hoists. Not far away from Letheringsett, but on the River Tas, is Saxlingham Thorpe Mill, and plate 19 shows the miller staffing the stone.

Now join the coast road, the A149, at Wells-next-the-Sea. Turn left here to follow the road through Holkham to Burnham Overy Mill, on a rather bad bend near Overy Staithe. It has quite an impressive brick

42 The remains of the waterpowered sawmill at Gunton Park, near Cromer, Norfolk, a timber building with a thatched roof of traditional Norfolk reed, probably built about 1800. It originally had two similar waterwheels. The existing wheel has been used to drive a reciprocating frame saw. A gear wheel on the axle tree drove the pulley wheel on the left. A belt from this drove the pulley at the top of the photograph, while another belt drove a further pulley at the rear, mounted on a cranked shaft which was linked to the saw frame. As the shaft turned the saw blade was pulled up and down. Timber to be sawn was mounted on a carriage which ran on rails through the sawmill

43 Bevel gearing, with the great spur wheel to the top of the photograph and the governor to the left, at Letheringsett Mill on the River Glaven, Norfolk

frontage, built in about 1795, but it no longer gives the impression of the hive of industry it must have been in the past. The three-storey mill, adjoining maltings, a barn, a row of cottages for millhands and a larger miller's house, form a large group of buildings. They have been owned by the National Trust since 1939, funds being provided by the Fellows Bequest and the Hon Alexandrina Pickover. There is an internal wheel and a steam boiler but no other machinery; it is, however, a pity that the public does not have any access to any part of the mill.

A short distance further on, leave the main road to take the B1355 to Fakenham, where there is a large mill with a curious mixture of buildings and methods. From Fakenham, take the A1067 to Bintree Mill, a four-storey building with an attractive bridge over the millpool. The sluice gates are of particular interest and are well geared. Nearby is Worthing Mill on the River Wensum, which has a good example of a governor (see plate 23). Also on the River Wensum is Elsing Mill, a very attractive building, half brick and half weatherboarded, with the finishing touches of decorated barge boards on the gable ends and a weather vane above. Continue along the A1067 to Lenwade, still on the River Wensum; the large mill here is worked by Sayer Bros Ltd.

Now take the road to East Dereham and then the A47 to Swaffham. A few miles beyond, still following the A47 but off to the left, is Narborough Mill, a large brick and tile building with a boarded lucam.

44 Burnham Overy Mill, Norfolk

45 The brick and weatherboarded Elsing Mill on the River Wensum, Norfolk

(*opposite*) 46 Narborough Mill, on the River Nar near Swaffham, Norfolk

(*right*) 47 A line-up of power: the interior of Narborough Mill showing the pit wheels

Some idea of the original capacity of this mill may be gained from the view of the gearing in plate 47. From King's Lynn there is a possible detour through Castle Rising to West Newton where the mill has been converted to a private dwelling. The undershot wheel has been retained and millstones form a staircase in the garden.

The journey across to the Peterborough area is a little longer but there are several mills well worth visiting. Maxey Mill, two miles south-west of Market Deeping, is still working regularly and is producing pig food. It is a three-storey building, part of which was built in about 1779. The breastshot wheel is a replacement made by a local miller, Mr F. E. Bird, in 1967. Molecey House Mill at West Deeping, north-east of Stamford, has a most interesting Poncelet wheel. Tickencote Mill is a little way up the A1 and Duddington Mill is to the south.

Returning towards the A1 will lead to Sacrewell Mill, half a mile to the east of the main road near its junction with the A47. Though this mill is not actually grinding, it is in working condition and is operated for a great number of visitors who also call to see an extensive collection of farm, rural craft and domestic bygones. It is one of six that used to work within a small area. At one time it had two wheels but now only one pitch-back wheel remains, 16ft in diameter and 5ft wide, with fifty-six buckets. The mill is administered by the William Scott Abbott Trust. A little further south there are mills at Water Newton and Elton.

48 Houghton Mill on the River Ouse, Cambridgeshire, now a popular youth hostel

49 Lode Mill in the grounds of Anglesey Abbey, Cambridgeshire, showing the mill-pond and flood-control sluice gate in the foreground

Now travel down the A1 to Huntingdon where the River Ouse has provided power for several mills. Hemingford is a weatherboarded mill with the mill house standing nearby, but Houghton Mill is perhaps better known, though it stands not on the Ouse but on one of its backwaters. When it last worked in 1930, it had three water-wheels. It could have fallen into dereliction but for the efforts of en-thusiasts who bought it and gave it to the National Trust in 1939. It was then leased to the Youth Hostels Association, who find it a most popular hostel among young people. The wheels have had to be removed and sluices inserted to control the water flow, but much of the machinery is still inside, including a governor. Another National Trust property in Cambridgeshire is Lode Mill, Anglesey Abbey.

From Houghton join the old Roman road, the A604, and travel into Cambridge. Leaving by the A10 and then the A130 you will find asso-ciations with Chaucer's miller at Trumpington. A few miles to the right, on the B1379, is Duxford Mill on the River Cam. It is privately owned and, though it has an internal wheel, 18ft in diameter by 9ft wide, there is little further machinery. The mill is not open to the public but the garden is open under the National Gardens Scheme. It is mentioned here because of its association with Charles Kingsley, who wrote parts of *The Water Babies* there in about 1860.

From Duxford, a detour might be made to Thaxted Mill on the A130, which has been considerably restored in recent years. Alternati-vely, travel straight on to Bishop's Stortford. Hallingbury Mill stands on an artificially cut mill stream off the main Stort navigation and was built in 1874. It has a low breast wheel 16ft in diameter and 7ft wide, with forty-eight buckets. There were four pairs of stones originally but only one pair remains complete. It can grind wholemeal flour and still has a governor control. Since the mill ceased full-time working in 1952, it has been restored and opened to the public in conjunction with canal pleasure cruises arranged by the mill owners, Lea and Stort Cruises Ltd.

This tour might well end with an investigation of what remains of the many mill sites in the Lea Valley between Hertford and the Thames. Horns Mill, near Hertford, had fulling stocks in the nine-teenth century used for impregnating skins with cod-liver oil in the preparation of chamois leather. Dickor, Ware Park, Stanstead, Lynch, Charlton, Broxbourne and Cheshunt are just some of the names of mill sites on the Upper Lea. Then there were the powder mills at Waltham Abbey, Silent Mill, Sewardstone Mill, Chingford, Tottenham and Walthamstow, and many more further down, all con-signed to historical records which show how much the country has depended on mills in the past.

THE EAST MIDLANDS

The fenlands around the Wash are not particularly suitable for using water power. In the Wolds, further north, however, the greater fall of water has been well used. Starting from Lincoln and taking the A46 north, one of the first villages is Nettleham. In the centre of the village, just off the main road, is Watermill House. No one remembers a wheel or working mill, but the site cannot be missed because a ford through the mill stream has to be crossed. The same thing happens further along, approaching Thorpe Mill, Tealby, three miles beyond Market Rasen, though here the traveller has to drive some distance along the stream, not simply across it. This mill worked until 1962 when the last miller, Percy Richardson, retired. It is fortunate that the mill was immediately taken over by Mr and Mrs J. Sivil who have maintained it in working order and still use it for grinding feeds for their own livestock. As in many mills, the whitewashed walls are almost a record book – pencilled notes such as 'new millstone August 1889', 'new stone October 4, 1907' and 'new arms for waterwheel, August 22, 1887', provide interesting historical detail. There is an old bell kept at the mill which was used to let the next miller downstream know when he could start to fill his pond and begin milling. When the bell sounded, milling had finished at Thorpe Mill, and that might be at any time of the day or night. Now, of course, the next working mill is too far away to hear!

There are some interesting and unusual features at Thorpe Mill. Percy Richardson used to call the wheel a three-quarter breast; it is one of a very few with two 'valves'. The upper valve or gate was normally used, causing the water to operate the wheel as a high breast wheel, but there was also another gate at the bottom so that the wheel could be undershot – a useful device if the reserve of water fell to a low level. No wonder Percy Richardson thought there could not be another mill like it. The stones turn 'against the sun', contrary to usual practice. Another uncommon detail is that the stones are 4ft 6in in diameter instead of the usual 4ft. Many years ago, when a new stone was required, Mr Richardson was quite relieved to find one for sale. However, while it was being hoisted up to the stone floor, he realised it was dressed the wrong way, so bit by bit it had to be re-dressed.

(left) 50 For the convenience of the miller – over the tail race at Thorpe Mill, Tealby, Lincolnshire; *(right)* 51 View of the wheel and tail race at Thorpe Mill

Now take the road into Louth and three miles to the north is Alvingham Mill. Close by is the site of Alvingham Priory with which the mill's early history is probably connected. Alvingham Mill is on the small River Lud which once powered thirteen mills, but although three other mill buildings remain, Alvingham is the only one left working. It is now run as a working museum by Ann and Phil Davies, who have done much restoration work, including the installation of a replacement pair of French stones which were retrieved from Yaddlethorpe watermill near Scunthorpe. The breastshot wheel, 11ft in diameter and 8ft wide, is made in cast iron with thirty-two wrought-iron buckets and elm boards. There is an unusual form of sack hoist using a bevel gear.

South of Louth, on the Great Eau river, is Ketsby Mill, which is used in connection with a large pig-breeding business; further down the same river is Aby Mill, driven by turbine. A few miles to the southwest is Stockworth Mill near Somersby, which has strong links with Alfred Lord Tennyson. Could this be the brook that inspired his great poem? Certainly Tennyson wrote about it in 'The Miller's Daughter'. Partney Mill on the River Lymm has unfortunately now gone, but between the A155 and the A1115 from Spilsby is the mill at Old Bolingbroke, probably once connected with nearby Bolingbroke Castle.

52 Alvingham Mill, now a working museum, on the River Lud near Louth, Lincoln-shire

Further on, in the attractive village of Kirkby Green, an old mill is reached by crossing a ford. Approaching Lincoln, there is evidence of yet another example of how today's major firms began with the power of a waterwheel. Park Mills, in Heighington, are now the large head-quarters of E. and T. R. Curtis Ltd which, since 1964, has been part of the nationwide group Rank Hovis McDougall Ltd; the business began in 1924 with a waterwheel on the Heighington Beck. On the Branston Beck at Springfield, Branston, there used to be a very narrow iron wheel which pumped water to Branston Hall and nearby houses, but this has now gone.

The Fosse Way (A46) through Newark-on-Trent takes the traveller to the Nottingham area. Nottingham has, in the past, made extensive use of the waterwheel to power its cotton and other textile mills. Ben-jamin and Charles Morley's mill began with a wheel but converted to a Boulton and Watt steam engine in 1790. The Davison and Hawks-ley mill in Arnold had a similar history; now only part of the 4 acre pond remains in the park. For the smaller type of mill, the Dover Beck provided much power; its largest was Lowdham Mill, beyond Arnold. It was in full working order until the 1940s, but has since been converted into an extension to the mill house, though the 20ft diameter wheel remains. Also on the Dover Beck is Hoveringham Mill (to the right of the A47). It was grinding until 1962, when it had to stop as the activities of local coal mines and gravel quarries had affec-ted the water table, resulting in a decline in the water supply. The mill's details have been fully recorded by students of the Department of Architecture at Nottingham University under the guidance of Norman Summers.

Further north, Retford has an interesting site at Bolham Mills on the Idle – a strange name for a river! The mills were making paper until about 1845 when Ashworth's began to use them for leather tanning. The power comes from two waterwheels. Another Nottinghamshire town that should thank the waterwheel for establishing much of the industry in the area is Mansfield on the River Maun. Bath Mill at one time made lace and is now a hosiery factory; Stanton's Mill and Hermitage Mill were powered from the same stream and what is now the large Metal Box Company began as a small mill grinding mustard in Rock Valley. King's Mill, going out towards Sutton-in-Ashfield, is on the site of an old manorial corn mill of which little remains. On the Derbyshire side of Mansfield, Pleasley had two mills close together on the River Meden, used, at various times, for corn, a forge and textiles, and more recently by Hollins' to produce Viyella. Just above the dam in the centre of the village, a small Methodist chapel was built which became known locally as the Dam Chapel!

53 Ollerton Mill on the River Maun, Nottinghamshire; today it produces animal feed

Nine miles north-east of Mansfield, also on the River Maun, is Ollerton Mill; this is still being worked by a low breast wheel which was renewed quite recently, and is producing animal feed. It has a good example of overdriven stones. Return through Sutton-in-Ashfield and Alfreton to reach the A6, then go on towards Derby.

Much of the development of Derby's use of water power is due to the work of George Sorocold, who set up a waterwheel there in 1692, on the site of an old gunpowder mill on the River Derwent, to establish an early waterworks. Nothing of this now remains, but so much evidence does exist of water power in Derbyshire that only a representative selection of information can be given here. Mention must be made of North Mill, Belper, a very large cotton mill built by Jebediah Strutt in 1803. It is one of the earliest iron-framed 'fireproof' mills still in existence. At night, when the mill is fully lit with its modern fluorescent lighting it provides an impressive sight from the A6 into Belper. The drawings of the early nineteenth-century part of the building show a waterwheel 18ft in diameter and 23ft wide with staggered buckets, appearing as six wheels locked together side by side. The drive was taken direct from the wheel rim by a pinion wheel transmitted by bevel gears throughout four floors.

Further north along the Derwent Valley is another landmark in the history of the waterwheel, at Cromford. Arkwright bought an old corn mill in 1771 and set up a cotton mill to put his water frames into action. Cromford Sough and Bonsall Brook ran through land leased by Arkwright and these enabled him to develop extensive water-powered mills with water taken across the road along a cast-iron launder. From the centre of Cromford, a drive along the A6 towards Matlock Bath will provide a good view of Arkwright's house, Willersley Castle, and also lead to Masson Mill which Arkwright developed after Cromford. It worked by waterwheel until converted to steam in the nineteenth century. Like other such mills it has, through a series of mergers, become part of the English Sewing Cotton Co and Courtaulds.

Back in Cromford village, there is an old paint-grinding mill opposite Tye's garage (the owners), with an overshot wheel over 14ft in diameter which is supplied by overhead iron pipes feeding water drawn from a reservoir much higher up the road. A little further out of Cromford on the A5012 is Cromford corn mill which worked until about 1930; it has now been acquired by the Arkwright Society who have partly restored the mill and use it as an information centre.

The Bakewell area, further north along the A6, was another centre for the use of water power. Rowsley Mill on the River Wye, which originally ground corn for the Haddon Hall estate, was run as a flour mill

54 The exterior of Rowsley Mill on the River Wye, Derbyshire

55 Inside the modern roller mill at Rowsley

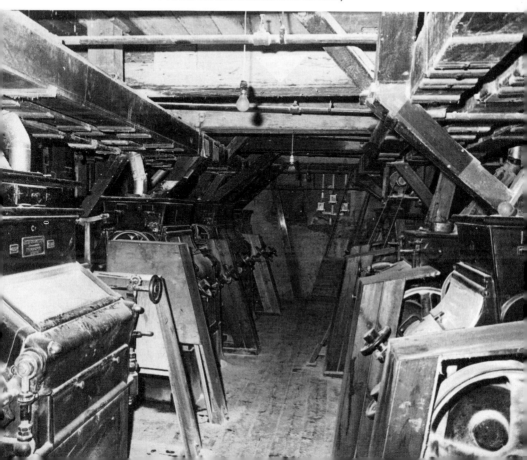

56 Undershot wheel removed but hopefully awaiting restoration at Victoria Mill on the River Wye, Bakewell, Derbyshire

by Caudwell Ltd until 1978. It had an undershot wheel in its early days but has been turbine-driven for most of this century. In Bakewell itself, Lumford Mill is another of Arkwright's ventures. It had two wheels, one 25ft in diameter and 18ft wide, and the other 21ft in diameter and 7ft wide. The larger one, a high breast wheel, held 10½ tons of water at a time. Later, when they were used by the Dujardin-Planté Battery Co Ltd, they drove a 66kV generator. The old 16ft diameter wheel at Victoria Mill on the Buxton Road, Bakewell has been removed and left standing outside for some years. The mill, which ground corn until the late 1940s, is, I believe, to be restored.

In Calver, on the road towards Sheffield, an impressive seven-storey hosiery mill was once powered by two 22ft diameter wheels which produced 80hp each. Another of Arkwright's successes may be found along the A623 towards Chapel-en-le-Frith, at Cressbrook Mill, Litton. It took water from the River Wye and had two large wheels. Steam power was added and then turbines, but now it is just a warehouse. The cotton mill in Litton has a varied history. Ellis Needham, one of its founders in about 1782, though notoriously mean, was declared bankrupt in 1815. The most unpleasant period of its history was during the early nineteenth century when it gained a reputation for the ill-treatment of London orphan apprentices.

Chapel-en-le-Frith deserves a place in any account which endeavours to show how much the waterwheel has contributed to the growth of industry. It has been the home of the New Hyde cotton mill, powered by steam for a long time, and the paper mills now belonging to Slacks of Hayfield. It is most interesting perhaps that Herbert Frood built a small waterwheel on a tiny stream in his garden to experiment in producing material for making brakes. He moved to Sovereign Mill in 1903, and now it has developed into the large Ferodo works producing brake linings.

A return through Buxton and along the A515 would make several exploratory detours possible. In Longnor is the workshop of the Harpur Crewe estate, powered by a 14ft 6in diameter pitch-back wheel. It has a pit wheel on either side and drives two circular saws, a planing machine and a mortising machine. Gradbach Mill is not easy to find and there is little reward after travelling the quarter of a mile along a gated road. It once had a 38ft diameter wheel with ninety-six buckets; now only a shell of a building remains, though it was offered for sale in 1978. On the way into Ashbourne it is worth halting in Hartington to look round an attractive village. On the outskirts is an old corn mill which has been the subject of a very skilful and attractive conversion. The leat has been restored to allow water from the River Dove to flow through the undershot wheel and a delightful garden.

On the return journey to Derby, a call may be made at Longford. An old corn mill here has more recently been used for grinding chicory for making instant coffee. It is an attractive building with leaded windows, looking more like a dwelling than a mill, and it is to be hoped that its future is guaranteed.

From Derby, continue yet again along the A6 towards Loughborough. One of the most historic mill sites of this area is to be found close to the A6 at Castle Donnington just before reaching Kegworth. King's Mills have a long and varied history but only ruins remain; it is clear, however, that at one time there were three wheels. No doubt the first purpose was as a corn mill, but for a time there was certainly a fulling mill here. Much more recently the mills have been used for grinding gypsum for the local plaster industry. The outstanding period at King's Mills was probably when, as a paper mill, they produced paper for banknotes for the Bank of England.

Down the A453, through Ashby-de-la-Zouch, lies Measham which once had one of the largest cotton mills in the area powered by a waterwheel. There was also a tape mill nearby on the River Mease, but little remains of this. Clock Mill near Measham Hall has been a corn mill for a very long time. Some renovation has been carried out; the mill stood empty for some years but was restarted as long ago as

1873. A few miles to the south, is an outstanding mill – Help Out Mill – at Odstone on the River Sence, so called, it seems, because it was able to help other mills when they ran dry. It has had a turbine since 1902 and is well equipped with a roller plant.

Now travel towards Leicester, keeping to the ring road to the north to reach the A6. There is a small mill between Glenfield and Anstey, and just north of Leicester, on the Loughborough–Leicester road, is Cossington Mill – a pleasant setting for a lunch but with little remaining to be seen of the original mill workings. It was in operation until 1928, after which it became quite dilapidated until being converted into a restaurant.

South of Leicester almost any route will lead through villages like Wigston and Enderby that once had thriving watermills, but take the A426 to Rugby. Just north of Rugby, near Churchover, is the ruin of a small overshot wheel with parts of a wooden launder; also near Rugby is Long Buckby Bottom Mill. Then follow the A45 to Daventry. Nearby Dodford Mill is fitted with a governor and its great spur wheel is a good example of clasp-arm construction.

To the south of Northampton, down the A43, Towcester Mill has a turbine. Further west, if a detour is desired, there is West Farndon Mill on the River Cherwell, north-east of Banbury. This mill in its heyday was very productive; steam was used for a time and later an oil engine. Though it remained intact until the 1960s, much of it has since been damaged or dismantled. Returning to the Northampton area, Upton Mill on the River Nene has mill and house looking very much as one building, both three storeys high. In Northampton, Rush Mill was used for driving a circular saw until about 1968.

When the Domesday Book was compiled, 170 mills appear to have been mentioned for Northamptonshire; today, the number of known mill sites is even higher than that. One mill with a history going back to Domesday is Bugbrooke Mill, recorded as the one with the highest value in the county. Latterly, Heygates Ltd, members of the Country Miller's Group, have operated it as a '20-sack' plant, keeping alive the spirit of a mill serving local farmers and providing a product for the local community.

One of the best-known mill sites in this area is likely to be the Billing aquadrome and touring caravan park to the east of Northampton. It includes a milling museum where the mill has been restored to working order to provide demonstrations for visitors. The building is early nineteenth-century, and by the time the mill ceased to work in the early 1960s it was in need of considerable repair. In 1965 a corn-milling museum was suggested; restoration began and the mill opened to the public in 1968. The wheel is a good example of the Poncelet type and is rather unusual in that it has six spokes. The water for Little Billing Mill is taken from the River Nene which has, in its history, powered many a mill. Among them were Floore Mill, Tunnell's Mill in Wellingborough and, further north, Woodford Mill east of Thrapston and Titchmarsh Mill on the north-west side. Further north still are Barnwell Mill near Oundle and Wadenhoe Mill in the same area. Even further on, towards Peterborough, is Pereo Mill which Mary Queen of Scots passed on her last journey from Milton near Peterborough to Fotheringhay Castle. When told the name of the mill she looked up, saw the turrets of the castle and exclaimed, 'Pereo, I perish!' It has been a very prosperous mill – in its early days, the tenant had to pay a rent of 1cwt of eels per year – but now there is little machinery left. This should be a good point from which to return to Leicester, Lincoln or whence we came.

THE NORTH AND WEST MIDLANDS

Sarehole Mill in Colebank Road, Hall Green, Birmingham is part of the Department of Archaeology, Ethnology and Birmingham History at the university. It provides another example of varied mill history. During the growth of Birmingham's metalworking industry, a second wheel was added and the mill was for a time leased by Matthew Boulton. In the nineteenth century, it returned completely to corn grinding which continued until 1919. It is in full working order again and open to the public. The north wheel is high breast and 12ft in diameter; the south wheel is overshot and just over 10ft in diameter.

South of Birmingham, stretches of the River Arrow, particularly around Studley and Alcester, have provided amazing power for mills. For many years there had been corn mills and forges driven by waterwheels. Around 1730, many of these were converted to needle mills as this industry grew. Only one remains complete – Forge Mill, Redditch – and ironically, it was probably the first to become a needle mill. It has been completely restored with considerable care by Redditch District Council and local enthusiasts. It is a pity, however, that it is possible to arrive and find the whole building locked and barred with no indication of opening times. It is surprising also, though not unique, that local inhabitants know little of it. Even a call at a local shop produced a very unconvincing reply: 'I think it's over there.' Actually it was almost within sight!

Three wheels were employed in the mill's early days. Then two breastshot wheels did the work but were eventually replaced by a wide overshot wheel with the tailwater taken away below ground. The capacity of the millpond was also increased to form what is known as a bottle pond, with intake and outlet at the same end. Machinery was driven from both sides of the overshot wheel through two separate buildings and two floors. Wire for needle making arrived rough and covered with scale; it had to be cut, cleaned and polished. Much of the cleaning was done in large wooden boxes, geared to the drive shaft from the wheel so that they rocked violently backwards and forwards. The needles were then made into bundles, wrapped in tight leather pouches with a lubricant and an abrasive powder, and rolled under a large stone. From the scouring mill, the needles were taken downstairs to the barrel shop for polishing in rotating barrels, then across into the other building for pointing and sharpening. Working conditions were appalling, involving dust, noise and the risk of accidents. In addition, there were times when, with the water level low, the men had to 'walk the wheel'. Stones could break and kill, and at least one worker at Redditch received fatal injuries in this way.

Ragley needle mill in Alcester also has some remains, including a 13ft 6in diameter breastshot wheel, but the water supply is by no means in good condition. Another mill of interest in the Alcester area is Great Alne Mill, a large mill that has employed a turbine and a Ruston diesel engine for most of this century. Its roller plant was removed when it closed down in the 1960s. Since then it has been, for a time, the workshop of a well-known millwright, Derek Ogden.

Further north, Tanworth Mill, which ended its working life in 1947, has been skilfully converted into a private dwelling. The gap between mill house and mill has been bridged to extend the accommodation, and the boarded lucam has been retained as an attractive window feature. The pond adds interest to the scene.

Of the hundreds of Warwickshire sites still providing some evidence of a mill, suffice it to mention but a few more. Guy's Cliffe Mill, once connected with Kenilworth Priory and believed to have a Saxon origin, is a popular restaurant. A small wheel still turns, though the main one has been removed. Rock Mill in Leamington Spa had a busy working life until 1961. Its two internal breastshot wheels were supplemented by a steam engine, diesel engine and electric motor at different times. It was a well-equipped mill with a good range of ancillary machinery.

There is a watermill in the small village of Chesterton near Leamington, close to the windmill that has recently been restored. Local inhabitants, I know, are concerned that it is falling into disrepair and hope that some form of restoration can be carried out. The Castle Mill in Warwick has no machinery left, but does still possess an external wheel. It has not worked as a mill since 1880 when a fire destroyed many of the interior fittings. Travelling south along the A46, a diversion may be made to see the old mill at Hampton Lucy near Stratford-upon-Avon. It is sad that Welford Mill, also near Stratford, has disappeared, at least as a mill. Mrs Strang, whose father was miller there, wrote the following description when she was eighty-three:

The mill was a busy mill with a large undershot wheel at each end. The river, dammed by a long weir and a disused lock passed under the road to drive the wheels and was regulated by sluice gates. The mill had a ground floor where large bins stood round the walls to receive the ground flour (beautiful smooth wooden shovels) and scales to weigh corn in and flour out. The 1st floor carried 5 pairs of large stones and an oat crusher and bean kibbler. On this floor was the main shaft with superb wooden axle and cog wheel, hard and polished to a velvet smoothness by constant use. The largest and heaviest pair of stones ground the wheat into flour for breadmaking. This flour was then sieved through a bolting cloth to extract the bran. The 2nd floor was the storage place and the beginning of the process of turning grain into flour. Here was a pulley wheel (wooden) and a beam round which a heavy chain wound to bring sacks of corn up through trap doors from the ground floor. This corn then flowed down through chutes into the hoppers over the stones on the 1st floor and the flour then by sleeves into attached sacks on the ground floor.

It was a busy mill – my father and a full time man worked in the mill and 2 carters were fully employed dealing with the orders. There were many small commissions from cottagers with allotments and a pig as well as the farmers who up till then had no machines of their own.

My father had a flair for making the most of the water power. He harnessed one wheel to a long shaft leading into what we called 'the shop' – a big workshop and shed. With this shaft powered by the mill wheel, he used a grindstone, a sawbench, a lathe and in the autumn an apple crushing contrivance for making pulp for a big cider press.

To a growing child it was all alive and of intense interest. Then came the First World War. This busy little business was bit by bit overcome by the changing times and general depression. My father died – my elder brother took over and looked like making a go of things but he died after only 18 months. His son demobbed after World War II showed no interest. He shut down the mill, sold the house, sold this and that and finally the mill building itself . . . A definite end to an era.

At least one of Welford's wheels has been rescued for use at Lutley Mill near Halesowen.

It is difficult to resist suggesting a detour to find one mill in the Vale of Evesham. Fladbury Mill, a few miles north-west of Evesham, has been converted, along with the mill house, into a large house in a very attractive setting. A hand-worked ferry boat adds to the calm and peaceful scene – at least on a summer's day!

From here, the route lies along the A44, through Worcester and Leominster, turning right at the junction with the A4110. Just off this road, near Mortimers Cross, is the small but interesting Lucton Mill. It was grinding animal feed until the 1940s when 'eine schöne Müllerin', aged about twenty, worked it alone. The sandstone and rubble building is eighteenth-century but has the air of being much older. Water comes along a leat from the River Lugg to drive the undershot wheel, which is quite broad for its diameter; it has eight wooden spokes, spoked iron hub plates and iron vanes. The mill has a dresser

57 The stone floor at Lucton Mill, Mortimers Cross, Herefordshire. In the foreground is the tun, encasing the millstones, with a crook string in front. Standing on the tun is the horse, behind which can be seen the hopper and the chute bringing down grain from the bin floor. In the background is a lay shaft, and on the left a belt drive from a lay shaft to an aspirator

for grading flour, operated by a belt drive. Another belt drive operates the sack hoist – all very compact. The mill is privately owned but has been placed in the care of the Department of the Environment. It is open to the public at rather limited times.

From Mortimers Cross, take the B4362 and B4361 to reach the A49. Cross this and take the A443 through Tenbury Wells. Newnham Mill, which is about four miles beyond Tenbury, is still producing wholemeal stone-ground flour. Now return a short distance along the A443, then turn right on to the B4214 to join the A4117 into Ludlow. Leave Ludlow by the A49 and after a short distance, turn right on to the B4365. This leads into Corve Dale. Along this valley there have been many mills – Halford Mill, Bache Mill, one near Middleton, Bitterley Mill, Farlow, Easthope and Hughley Mills. In the middle of the valley, just through the village of Munslow, is Broadstone Mill. This mill has been fully recorded and drawn by Dr Cyril Boucher, an outstanding authority on the subject. The overshot wheel and some machinery have now gone, since the mill has not worked since the 1930s. On the other side of the River Corve, on Pye Brook, is Bouldon Mill which is a little more complete.

58 Overshot wheel at Walkmill Farm, Leebotwood, Salop

From Broadstone, there is a minor road to the left through Long-ville-in-the-Dale, Gretton, and Cardington back on to the main A49 and hence into Leebotwood. To the west of the main road, a little to the north, is a turning to Walkmills. Walkmill Farm is not easy to find and not on a through road, but it has a fine overshot wheel which has been providing electricity for the farm for some time. When I called recently, the generator was about to be altered to provide a three-phase supply. The wheel is about 20ft in diameter but only 2ft wide, with forty-eight buckets. There is a good fall of water so a large pond is not necessary. This mill is privately owned but, as at many mill sites, my arrival was most warmly received.

Through Much Wenlock and then to the Ironbridge and Coal-brookdale area is a journey that a watermill enthusiast might con-sider. The contribution to waterwheel development made in this area by the great ironmasters, Wilkinson and Darby, has been mentioned in Part One. Alas, although outstanding success has been achieved in creating what has been widely acclaimed as one of the finest industrial museums in Europe, the waterwheel that provided the air for the blast furnaces is no longer there – only sufficient evidence to indicate its whereabouts in the past.

From Ironbridge, take the A518 to Stafford. A few miles to the north-west is Worston Farm Mill, Great Bridgeford, Stafford. The mill worked regularly until about 1970; since then the type of farming has been changed and the mill has not been used. It is, however, in fairly good condition and has an extremely good range of quite modern ancillary equipment. The present private owner has every intention of retaining the mill in a complete form.

Stone, best reached by taking the A34, has been another centre to use water power extensively and for a variety of purposes. Top Mill was a flint mill very similar to Cheddleton, described below, with two wheels side by side, but overshot. Ivy Mill ground bone for making bone china until 1965, though it has also been used as a paper mill. Hayes Mill was another bone mill. Weaver's Mill has been converted from an overshot wheel to a turbine and electricity to drive four pairs of stones for flour and one for shelling oats; in a separate building, another wheel was once used to grind flint. South-east of Stone, Coton Mill in Milwich is unworkable but has the less common pitch-back wheel and also an unusual arrangement of slip cogs to throw the stone nuts out of gear.

One of the outstanding mills in this area is without doubt Cheddle-ton flint mill, on the A520 about four miles south of Leek. This was a well chosen site, since water is supplied by the River Churnet and it is also the point of junction with the Caldon branch of James Brindley's Trent and Mersey Canal; both power and transport were therefore available. Probably the most interesting and attractive feature is the existence of twin mills – a wheel on each side of the river with a central pillar supporting the axle of both. Originally, only a corn mill existed on one side; then a flint mill was added and eventually the corn mill was converted to flint as well. Both wheels are low breasts, one with thirty-six L-shaped floats and the other with forty similar floats. The machinery is in heavy proportions but faces heavy work in driving large boulders round the pans, which are 11ft and 14ft in diameter. The mills closed down in 1963, but in 1967 restoration work began. Now, after considerable and admirable work by the Cheddleton Flint Mill Industrial Heritage Trust, the mills are a worthy tribute to the pottery industry and well worth visiting.

Also on the River Churnet and having associations with James Brindley is the corn mill in Leek, commonly known as Brindley Mill; it is at the bottom of the hill leaving Leek by the A523 for Macclesfield. The inscription 'JB 1752' is carved over a first-floor window. A small but elegant-looking building, it may well be missed because of the surrounding large buildings. The paddle wheel can be seen at the rear, reached along a nearby side road. After the mill had been derelict for many years, restoration work was carried out between 1970 and 1974. It is now open to the public and can grind small quantities of corn for demonstration.

59 The twin wheels at Cheddleton flint mills on the River Churnet, Staffordshire

60 The grinding pan at Cheddleton

61 Brindley Mill at Leek, Staffordshire

Continue along the Macclesfield road but take the A54 into Congleton, which also has connections with James Brindley and with grinding stone. The River Dane runs through the town, and this has provided power for several mills within a short distance, though little is now left. One wheel was removed some years ago when a child was killed by it. Havannah Mill was demolished in 1975 and R. H. Lowe's mill, where Brindley is said to have built a wheel, is gradually losing the mill race.

Now take the A534 into Sandbach. The large mill here, on the River Wheelock, was once worked by a 10ft diameter overshot wheel, then by a beam engine and more recently by electricity. Warmingham Mill, just a few miles to the north, used to grind coconut shells for making plastics but has been converted into a craft centre. A turbine replaced the undershot wheel many years ago.

Returning south to the Potteries, Knypersley Mill was rebuilt by the Trent and Mersey Canal Co in 1823 when Knypersley Reservoir was built. A high breast wheel operated four pairs of stones, of which there are some remains. Still further south, Burndhurst Mill, Uttoxeter, has been altered; the undershot wheel was enclosed but is now opened up and is more decorative than functional. Mayfield cotton mill has been a corn mill and a leather mill; it now has a turbine.

YORKSHIRE

The development of industry in Sheffield, particularly in steel, owes much to the waterwheel. It is fitting, therefore, that the City Museums Department has preserved one of its more interesting examples in an attractive way for visitors to appreciate – Abbeydale Industrial Hamlet on the main Sheffield to Bakewell road (A621). It was principally a scythe works, on the River Sheaf, but a complete set of workshops and cottages are neatly arranged around a courtyard. Several wheels have been used: one to work the tilt-hammers, cutting shears and a two-cylinder blowing machine for the forge, the others to turn grindstones. In recent years, the enthusiasm of many local government bodies and organisations for restoration has grown, but Sheffield's project goes back as far as 1961 and was no mean task after such a large site, having worked for at least 160 years, had been decaying for around twenty-seven years.

The Shepherd wheel, east of the city, has also been restored. An 18ft cast-iron overshot wheel, it powered two workshops. Notice that the long row of windows is arranged on one side of the workshop so that light shone on to the working faces of the grindstones. The air inside the building would have been thick with flying dust.

In the Loxley Valley there are at least eight wheel sites. At Rowel Bridge there were two wheels; the Olive paper mill also had a grinding mill; Low Matlock had an overshot wheel, one of the last in the valley to work; Wisewood Forge once had four wheels and six tilt-hammers, the last one remaining until 1964. The rolling mills nearby were converted to turbine drive at some time, but the whole site is now quite different. Malin Bridge corn mill has perhaps the only undershot wheel still in existence in the area.

Apart from Abbeydale, the Little London Works was also on the River Sheaf and also had a pitch-back wheel. Millhouses corn mill is perhaps the oldest site on the Sheaf and in the area, since it was probably used by the monks of Beauchief Abbey. Sharrow snuff mill is the last to work productively in Sheffield: pestle and mortar mills are powered by an overshot wheel. South of the city, Eckington has been a mini-version of Sheffield's industry. Within two miles of the Mossbeck Brook there were eight or nine dams for grinding mills and forges for scythe and sickle making, a flourishing export trade in the nineteenth century. Garden Supplies Ltd, makers of 'Scythette', now occupy one of the sites.

Going north from the city centre along the A61 and the A629, there is a forge site on the River Don at Wortley. The tilt-hammers here are quite different from those at Abbeydale since the wheel acts at a point halfway along the hammers. A wooden beam on top of each hammer acts as a spring and thus increases the force of the blow. The forge made iron wire for nails, but became particularly productive as the railways developed, making chains and axles.

Now return to the A61 from Sheffield which goes through Barnsley. Two miles south of Barnsley, Worsbrough Mill has quite recently been returned to action as a restored mill and working museum by the South Yorkshire County Council. The 16ft diameter cast-iron overshot wheel, using water from the River Dove, operates the older stones, but two pairs were added during the nineteenth century. These, an oat roller, a centrifugal reel separator and a sack hoist are powered by a 1911 Hornsby 24 litre hot-bulb oil engine. It is a centre for country fairs and rural crafts such as wooden bucket and clog making, so it is a popular place for family outings. The A61 continues right through to Leeds.

Leeds City Council is, at the time of writing, engaged in establishing an industrial museum at Arnley Mills in Canal Road. It is intended that it should contain a fulling mill and a corn mill. Bradford also has its industrial museum at Moorside Mills; in the Motive Power Gallery, exhibits include a breastshot wheel, but its function is demonstrated by electric motor.

From Bradford, take the road through Keighley to Lothersdale where you will find Dale End Mills, owned by James Wilson and Son. The enterprise began as a small corn mill, but grew into a large spinning and weaving mill, with a 48ft diameter wheel added in 1860. With the addition of a steam engine it was capable of powering over a hundred looms. Though not used, the wheel can still be seen by arrangement at the mill shop. High Corn Mills in Skipton have now become the George Leatt Industrial and Folk Museum. Until 1964, the mills were part of Skipton Castle estate. The machinery has been restored and one of the two waterwheels now drives two pairs of stones.

If it is possible to take more time to appreciate the beauty of the Dales, then a recommended place to stay is at Scalegill in Kirkby Malham, just a little further north, through Skipton. Scalegill watermill and its adjacent cottages have been converted into cottages and flats for holiday visitors. In about 1924, the wheel and the shaft,

62 The great pitch-back wheel at Foster Beck Mill, Pateley Bridge, Yorkshire

which was solid brass and bronze, were sold to pay for reroofing. However, the River Aire still flows past, and this drives turbines that provide much of the electricity. It is also a good spot for bird-watching and fishing. Not far away is Otterburn tweed mill. This does not now use its original water power but may still have the traditional teasels — to raise the nap of the cloth — and fulling stocks in use for visitors to see.

An alternative can be found in Nidderdale, north-west of Harrogate. Foster Beck Mill used to be a hemp mill and worked until the 1960s. Now, as the Watermill Inn, it is recommended as a restaurant and small hotel. It still has a magnificent pitch-back wheel but the machinery has been removed. While in this area, the visitor is almost certain to visit Fountains Abbey, and not far away, in Galphay on the River Laver, is a mill that was working until 1956. It may still be complete; it had facilities for powering several pieces of equipment, such as a circular saw, from the wheel.

Those who have toured with a caravan or camped in the area will doubtless know of Sleninford Mill in North Stainley, just north of Ripon on the River Ure. This mill has not worked since 1950, but its wheel and equipment are largely complete.

Now take the road into Ripon, leaving by the B6265 to join the A1 or cross it to join the old Dere Street down to the A59 into York. Castle Museum in York has become well known for the attractive way in which it depicts how ordinary people have lived in the past. It includes among the exhibits an overshot wheel which drives one pair of stones. The wheel and machinery were moved to the museum in 1953 after being removed from Raindale, six miles north of Pickering on the North Yorkshire Moors. Stone-ground flour is available for sale, though it is not ground in the museum.

Some ten miles or so north of York, in the pretty village of Stillington, the watermill has been imaginatively converted into a private dwelling. The pit wheel and wallower still form part of the lounge furniture, and the upright shaft penetrates the floor. Of the original stones, one has been topped with a circular cushion and another forms the base for the spiral staircase.

The area, particularly to the east, is not fortunate in having any well preserved examples of its once generous number of mill sites. Driffield had several, including a bobbin mill driving wood-turning lathes. The mill at Nafferton is just to the north, though its breastshot wheel has not worked for some time.

THE NORTH-WEST

If the area around Manchester had not had the use of the waterwheel in the past, how vastly different it might be today! Take Stockport, for example. There were water-powered mills at Adlington Square, Brinksway Mills, Ashton's Mill in Portwood (which had two wheels), Sheepwash Mill and Logwood Mill (grinding dyestuff). Park Mill in Warren Street, Adswood, Offerton, Portwood and Reddish Vale Mills all ground corn at one time. It would not make particularly interesting reading to add similar lists for places such as Clitheroe, Littleborough, Bury, Rochdale, Heywood and Chorley. The point is clear – waterwheels have littered the area, serving a wide range of purposes. Caton once had a forge mill, and Storey's of Lancaster was once Low Mill cotton mill, powered by a wheel. Paton and Baldwin Ltd in Ellel is on the site of an old corn mill, and at Oakenclough paper mills, now belonging to Harold Jackson Ltd, the site at least of an old waterwheel can be seen.

One of the oldest mills in the area is Higher Mill in Helmshore, near Haslingden in Rossendale. It still has its fulling stocks for shrinking and matting the cloth, powered by a 17ft diameter pitch-back wheel.

Among the wheels that have been restored in this area is one that has been connected with the bleaching industry. Originally at Black Rock Mill, Turtons Bottom, Edgeworth, the wheel has been removed to the grounds of Turton Tower, one of Blackburn's branch museums. It was almost buried when restoration plans were made and has presented a small team of Turton Local History Society members with considerable problems. The wheel is 14ft in diameter by 6ft wide and has ventilated buckets. It should be available shortly for the public to see.

Some way out to the south of this area, just off the A534 Wrexham to Nantwich road near Farndon, Stretton Mill has been restored and is in the care of Cheshire County Museum Service. It worked until 1959 and then became derelict. Much of the restoration work was carried out by a Job Creation team under the expert guidance of Dr Cyril Boucher, lately of the Department of Building, University of Manchester Institute of Science and Technology. It has a breastshot wheel which is enclosed in a stone extension added in 1819. The mill

63 (*above*) 'Calm as a mill-pond': Stretton Mill, Cheshire

64 The restoration of Bunbury Mill, Cheshire, by the North-West Water Authority, showing the new sluice gates

has been open to the public in the summer months since 1978. A barn which was previously used as a workshop has been restored and accommodates an exhibition and the publications sales counter.

Three miles south-east of Tarporley, between the A49 and A51, there is another example of restoration work at Bunbury Mill, this time by the North-West Water Authority assisted by a Job Creation team and students at Runcorn Skills Centre. The mill worked until 1960, when a tree wedged in the flood gate after heavy rains, sweeping it away and causing the pond to empty. By 1977 it was back to life again and open to the public.

Across on the east side of the M6 near Holmes Chapel is a mill of a completely different character – Swettenham. Those who wish to see a working mill in what might be described as a natural state will find it here. At the entrance is a sign displaying the name:

DAFFODIL DELL
KNOWN THE WORLD OVER

In the springtime visitors can admire the beauty of nothing short of a 'host of golden daffodils', planted beside the stream by the owner, Wilf Lancaster. There are thousands of snowdrops, too, earlier in the season. The building is part brick and part timber-framed, and the earliest date inscribed on it reads 'T. S. 1675'. The 14ft diameter iron pitch-back wheel turns regularly. It can drive any of the five pairs of stones, one a shelling pair, but is frequently used with a belt drive to a horizontal sawmill outside, surrounded by planks of elm, yew and other local timbers. Mr Lancaster also uses it connected to a generator to provide electricity for the mill and farm. I was talking with him one day when the small light bulb dangling above us went strangely dim. 'It must be ten to five,' he said. 'It's milking time. I'd better go and give them a drop more water!' Off he went to adjust the penstock control gate. The wheel is not easy to get to and fits rather closely to the wall. Mr Lancaster tells a tale of a visit he made once to another nearby mill with a similar wheel. 'Don't talk to me about wheels close to the wall,' the miller warned him. Then the story came out. In a very bad winter, his wheel had become frozen to the wall. The only way to free it was to climb inside and burn some oily rags. Just as the fire got alight, the wheel began to turn – with the miller inside. What a predicament to be in! Mr Lancaster is proud of the fact that he recently used his stones to grind some corn that had been sown, grown and gathered by children at Peover Church. The children took the flour home and baked some unleavened bread which was eaten at their Confirmation service.

Another mill not far away which is still capable of working is Bate

Mill near Over Peover. The undershot wheel has been repaired and there is also a 35hp Crossley diesel engine as well as an electric motor. However, the miller's attention has now turned to trout farming in the mill stream.

Further east, Danewood Mills, Bosely, are now a large concern producing wood flour for making plastics. James Brindley is said to have had connections with this mill when it was used for copper rolling and may have had six wheels. Brindley was also involved, at an early age, in building one of the mills in Wildboarclough. He walked into Manchester on his day off, memorised the details of Smedley Mill there, then designed Lower Crag Mill. The large administrative building is all that remains. Folly Mill in Wincle has an interesting tale attached to it. After two mills had been washed away by floods, the story goes that the miller's wife said it would be folly to build again. He ignored the warning, but died before he could use the new mill.

Macclesfield's silk mills used water power. An ingenious system was used to control the speed of the 16ft diameter wheel in Frost's Park Green Mill. A double-faced clock was used, with the top face driven by the waterwheel and the bottom face by a normal clock mechanism. By comparing the times, the flow of water could be maintained at the correct level. The device was built in 1810 and is now in the North-Western Museum of Science and Industry in Manchester.

One of the most interesting mills in the area is, without doubt, Nether Alderley Mill on the A34 two miles south of Alderley Edge.

65 Surplus power: the overflow from the sluice control at Swettenham Mill, Cheshire

66 Nether Alderley Mill, Cheshire

The mill is by the roadside, and because the rear wall forms the dam, the appearance is unusual. A long, sloping roof, broken only by four small dormer windows, sweeps down almost to ground level. There's not a drop of water in sight; the tailwater runs under the road. The interior is equally unique: it has a staircase of wheels. Water flows first on to a 12ft diameter overshot wheel; its tail race is the flume for a second overshot wheel of a similar size, and markings on the wall suggest that a third wheel existed at some time. The two wheels can be coupled together by a lay shaft. The stones are supported on a cast-iron hursting; two pairs are underdriven and two require overdrift. Alongside the mill was a drying kiln. The upper floor of the kiln has long since been lost, but there is sufficient in the vaulted basement for the visitor to imagine it working. The mill was presented to the National Trust some years after it ceased to work. Since then, sterling work in restoring it to working order has been done by Dr Boucher and his son Andrew. The mill opens regularly to visitors.

Two miles north of Wilmslow, not far from Manchester Airport, is Quarry Bank cotton mill in Styal. When built by Samuel Greg in the eighteenth century, it was powered by waterwheel. A turbine and modern machinery were installed much later. Quite recently an ambitious programme was undertaken to create a museum of the early water-powered cotton industry. This is open to the public and owned by the National Trust.

THE ISLE OF MAN

The Lady Isabella wheel at Laxey is probably the best known and largest wheel in the world, with the possible exception of Noira wheels used for irrigation in the Middle East. It was built in 1854 by Robert Casement to pump water from the shafts of local lead mines. Andres Jespersen, the Danish authority on the subject, prepared an admirably detailed description of the wheel and its design theory for the centenary celebrations. He discusses the case for deciding to construct a pitch-back wheel. One advantage was that the length of the wooden trough on top of the wheel could be reduced by about 40ft, and at a height of 72ft 6in above ground it is desirable to avoid water blowing out of the buckets. Water collected from mountain streams was carried along pipes inside the white tower and poured into the trough above the wheel.

The wheel turned at 2rpm and could pump 250 gallons of water from a depth of 200 fathoms in that time. The crank had a 10ft stroke connected to a line of rods extending 600ft to the top of the pit. The rods were of oak strapped together with wrought-iron plates. It was named the Lady Isabella wheel in honour of the wife of the Governor at the time of the opening. Its working life ended in 1929 and it was idle for about ten years, during which time it suffered more damage than it would have done turning twice every minute. It was gradually restored and is now, of course, a popular and well maintained tourist attraction. One year it appears vermilion, having been coated with iron oxide, and the following year it is treated with red lead.

Other mills on the island are overshadowed in more ways than one. To the south there is Kentraugh Mill at Colby. This has been restored and is working, but although the breastshot wheel is in position, electric power is used for demonstrations. Near the west coast, Glenfaba Mill near Peel has a breastshot wheel used to generate electricity. Both these mills are privately owned.

The Isle of Man Forestry, Mines and Lands Board owns the Cregg Mill at Silverdale, which is adjacent to a boating pool and pleasure park. It appears to work, but is not in a well-restored condition. It was grinding corn until about 1940.

67 The Lady Isabella pitch-back wheel at Laxey, Isle of Man

THE LAKE DISTRICT

The Lake District abounds with energy from its streams and rivers. One of the fastest flowing rivers in the country is said to be the Kent, which falls 1,000ft in about twenty-five miles. That could mean, allowing an average head of water of 10ft, the possibility of a mill every quarter of a mile. The total number of sites used in this area at one time or another could well be seven hundred or so, yet not one is included in the Domesday list! Another surprising fact about water power here is the variety of duties the mills had to perform. For example, the mill at Troutbeck Bridge, just south of Ambleside, was a fulling mill before 1390; a corn mill in 1649; a paper mill in 1673; a flax mill in 1788; a bobbin mill in 1829; and generated electricity from 1900 to 1947.

The manufacture of gunpowder — usually confined to the more remote areas of the country, of course — was quite widespread in the Lake District, developing considerably in the nineteenth century. Gatebeck is one example: a new method of producing saltpetre by adding muriate of potash to nitric soda in 1865 added to its expansion. Sedgwick, also on the River Kent, was producing over 20 tons of gunpowder per week in 1914 at its nine mills powered by a 36ft and a 20ft diameter wheel. Later, there were seven turbines. Low-wood and Elterwater are further examples of gunpowder works.

High on the list of water-powered industries were the forges and ironworks. Take just one example of many — Cleator on the River Ehen near Whitehaven. Spade Forge produced edge tools, particularly spades and shovels, for mining and quarry work. There are some remains at Forge Garage. It was in Cleator that Fairbairn installed one of his 'ventilated' wheels, 22ft in diameter and 20ft wide, in 1840; it produced 175hp. Further north, Cockermouth has been fortunate to have the power of the River Cocker. Double Mills are now a youth hostel and little remains of the machinery; there were twin wheels, one on each bank. Also in the town were two flax mills and a woollen mill that became a tannery.

From Cockermouth, enjoy the journey along the Whinlatter Pass to Keswick. Brigham Forge and several other mills in Keswick have been powered by waterwheel, including the well-known pencil mill. Cross now to Penrith and take the A686. A few miles to the north-east of Penrith in a quiet spot is Little Salkeld Mill. If the visitor is anxious to find out how a mill works, see it in production, purchase a sample of its wholewheat flour and taste it to guarantee satisfaction on the spot – then here is an outstanding example. The Factory Acts posters and the miller's hard hat and visor may look somewhat incongruous in this context, but are necessities in these days of the Health and Safety at Work Act. The mill had been little used for a number of years when the owner retired in 1974. However, it was in a good condition and little time was lost by the new owners in giving it a thorough overhaul and carrying out the necessary restoration work. A fairly long leat brings water from the Sunnygill Beck on to the two overshot wheels, both 12ft in diameter. The narrower one drives the oatmeal stones while the wider one, with twice as much power, drives two pairs of stones, the sack hoist and a crushing mill. There is an interesting old winnowing machine on the first floor, and the wooden worm drive that turns a long wooden shaft with ropes attached for lifting runner stones is a piece of equipment not usually found outside this area.

The return route follows the edge of Ullswater into Troutbeck Bridge, which has already been mentioned. At this point there are areas of interest in either direction. Ambleside, at the north end of Lake Windermere, is always attractive, and many visitors will know of the existence of the overshot wheel at the pottery and gift shop there. The wheel has been restored, but the machinery no longer exists. It once worked in conjunction with nearby Bark Mill which ground bark for the Fisherbeck tannery. Fulling mills also thrived in the area, as did Horrax's bobbin mill.

Now this introduces a most important aspect of Cumbrian water-wheel power – its use for turning bobbins. With the growth of the Lancashire, Yorkshire and Derbyshire textile trade the demand for wooden bobbins was tremendous. Bobbin mills sprang up and existing mills were converted. Coppice barns stood nearby to store the drying timber gleaned from local coppices, mainly birch. In their greed, employers frequently failed to avoid poor working conditions and child slavery. Boys did the rough turning and preparatory work in dust, dirt and dim light. Staveley was a leading centre: at Gatefoot Mills, the average output per man was ninety gross of bobbins per week. But perhaps the best example is Stott Park, near the west bank of Lake Windermere. Originally powered by a 32ft diameter high breast wheel, the mill could accommodate twenty-five lathes and sixty-three workers. J. R. Coward and J. Iveson now operate on the site, using mainly automatic lathes.

South of Kendal at Gallowbarrow is Natland Beck Mill. This may appear to be rather dilapidated, but it has the advantage of being clearly visible from the roadside. It has not ground corn since 1910; before that time it was highly successful, being adjacent to the canal and wharf. For a time it generated electricity. Another mill easily seen from the roadside is Burnt Mill, about 1½ miles from Sedbergh.

Just off the A6 near Milnthorpe is Heron Mill on the River Bela. A 14ft diameter high breast wheel drives four pairs of stones at this mill, which operated commercially until 1955. Like many mills, its history goes back a long way and has monastic connections. The present building is mid-eighteenth-century and includes a good example of a corn-drying kiln. Recently, the mill has undergone careful restoration; it is now open to the public, operated by the Heron Corn Mill– Beetham Trust, and is reached by crossing a footbridge behind Waterhouse Mills on the opposite bank of the river. Also within this area are two other mills worthy of note. At Lupton, near the A65 Kirby Lonsdale road, is a small but good example of a corn mill with breastshot wheel; it was in operation until 1964. On the north side of the A590 is Witherslack Mill, in a very picturesque setting. It has a narrow 22ft diameter pitch-back wheel but is not working since most of the machinery has been removed.

68 The double wheels at Eskdale Mill, Boot, in Cumbria. The overshot wheel on the right has been restored

There are two other mills in Cumbria which have been restored and are open to the public. Muncaster Mill is delightfully situated near the River Mite, about one mile north of Ravenglass, and can be reached by the Ravenglass and Eskdale miniature railway. It flourished until 1954 but plodded on until 1961. The railway company acquired it in 1975 and with the help of Task Force North, a part of the Job Creation Scheme, carried out a thorough restoration of the mill. It includes a kiln for drying grain, particularly oats. One pair of stones is used for shelling – the initial husking of oats – after which the hulled oats, known as groats, pass through a dust machine and husk fan. Then, via the elevator, they are taken through the second pair of stones, and finally sieved in a shaker-screen to produce oatmeal. The third pair of stones, French burr, grinds wheat, and is used in conjunction with a dresser for separating various grades of flour.

About a quarter of a mile from Dalegarth Station at the head of the miniature railway is Eskdale Mill in the delightful village of Boot – and it is best to walk that quarter-mile! Cumbria County Council Planning Department is to be complimented on the restoration work undertaken since the council acquired the mill in 1972. It has two 'in line' 12ft diameter overshot wheels fed by a leat from the Whillan Beck. The stones are a little unusual, being 5ft in diameter.

THE NORTH-EAST

Starting our tour in Cleveland, it is encouraging to be able to begin with a contribution to mill preservation by young people. Students from the South Park Sixth Form College, under John Harrison, their Head of Technical Studies, have been working on the preservation of Tucketts Mill, Guisborough. The mill worked until 1960; now, as part of a caravan park, it will house a museum.

Towards the coast, along the A173 and A174, is Kilton Mill near Loftus, which worked until 1942. Reg Richardson was one of the last millers there. He remembers the 16ft diameter wheel, so well balanced that it was possible to push it round by hand – something which, as a boy, he took great pride in doing as a feat of strength! His father used to charge 6d per sack for collecting grain, grinding it and then delivering it back to the farmers. At busy times of the year, Mr Richardson spent many hours at night looking after the grinding as the mill was kept running twenty-four hours a day – as long as the water supply held out. The only light in the mill was from a few candles; for a boy of ten or eleven it was creepy and ghost-like!

Further north, through Middlesbrough and Bishop Auckland, is Killhope waterwheel in Upper Weardale. It was built to power a lead-ore dressing works which is now in ruins. But the 34ft diameter over-shot wheel is a good example and is set, for all to see, in what is now a popular picnic area. From Weardale, take the A690 into Durham. Here, naturally, the cathedral is bound to attract visitors' attention; but within its shadow, at the foot of the precipice on which it stands, are the remains of two mills, one on each side of the weir. The old monastic mill, of which records go back for centuries, stands nearest to the cathedral; it once had a large overshot wheel, but all the machinery has gone. Of the other mill, only the foundations are left.

The A1 from Durham leads into Newcastle upon Tyne, once an area with not only corn mills but also several flint mills driven by waterwheel. In the park at Jesmond Dene are the ruins of one of these flint mills. Further along the A1, about ten miles beyond Morpeth, is Felton Mill on the River Coquet. It has an old paddle wheel, as can be seen in plate 16, which also shows clearly the jack ring used for putting the stone nut out of gear.

69 Felton Mill on the River Coquet, Northumbria

70 Twizel Mill on the River Till, Northumbria

From Felton, the B6345 crosses to the A697. It is a fairly lengthy journey towards the border at Coldstream, but one that is well worthwhile to approach the River Till area. Take the B6354 off to the right after passing through Milfield; then turn left just beyond the point where the road crosses the river. A little further on is Heatherslaw Mill, which consists of two separate mills with undershot wheels in one main building. They worked commercially until 1949 but are now cared for by a trust which in 1975 commenced restoration work on the mills, granary, kiln and stables. A little further north is Ford forge mill, also on the River Till. From here, one alternative would be to explore the more northerly parts of the River Till, but you may like to explore the site of the Battle of Flodden Field (1513), just south of Branxton, because it has some connection with the next mill on the tour – Twizel Mill. To reach this, take the A697 again to pass through Cornhill-on-Tweed and then the A698 to Twizel Bridge, once a vital point for crossing the River Till, particularly during disputes across the border. About half a mile or so south of the bridge is Twizel Mill, unfortunately no longer working.

SCOTLAND

Well over 200 sites exist in Scotland where a waterwheel or some evidence of one can be found; the total figure may be closer to 300. Many are small farm mills used for threshing or for meal; many had a kiln attached. Some of these are still working, but in some cases they are in remote areas and therefore not easily accessible. Then there are the great centres of milling and water power like Perth with its flour mills and foundry, Rothesay, Johnstone and Stanley with their cotton mills, and the Carron works for iron to which John Smeaton made such a valuable contribution.

The tour may begin at the border at Coldstream, Berwickshire, where an old grain mill may still have its machinery and wheel intact. The A698 to Berwick and then the A1 and the A1107 run into Eyemouth; here there is a Victorian mill which has been modernised but still has its two large overshot wheels. Nearby Ayton Castle has an old watermill in its grounds. Continuing on the A1 you will bypass Dunbar to reach East Linton, where to the right is one of the country's outstanding mills, the colourful and impressive Preston Mill on the River Tyne. The red pantile roof of the mill and the conical roof of the adjoining kiln provide colour and pattern that have attracted many photographers and painters. Since 1950 it has been owned by the National Trust for Scotland, and since 1966 Rank Hovis McDougall Ltd have not only contributed considerably to the mill's maintenance and repair, but have also generously offered experienced millers the opportunity to retire to the mill as custodians, demonstrating the working of the mill and keeping the wheel – 13ft in diameter and 3ft 2in wide – in running order.

Further along in the Haddington area, still in East Lothian, is the Mault or Kirk watermill at Poldrate. Through the courageous efforts of the Lamp of Lothian Collegiate Trust, this mill was saved from demolition some years ago and is now a community centre. The wheels still turn some of the machinery and demonstrations are given occasionally.

A detour could be made here down to Blyth Bridge, where the mill on Tarth Water is now part of an attractive hotel, dating back to 1812. The wheel, which is part cast iron and part wood, is well pre-

71 Preston Mill, East Linton, in East Lothian, showing the wheel on the extreme right and the kiln on the left

served, along with the machinery and stones. Carved on an outside wall is 'Meal per peck this year 2/6'. Nearby, a sawmill is worked by its 14ft diameter overshot wheel.

The site of the famous Carron ironworks in the Falkirk area is en route for the Inverallan Mill, Bridge of Allan, near Stirling. This mill is now owned by the Keir and Cawder Estates Ltd, who experienced such considerable difficulty, because of fire regulations, in obtaining planning permission for its use as an office that they decided to remove the machinery. However, all is not lost, because the mill at Blair Atholl is now in full working order and open to the public, making use of stones and machinery from Inverallan.

The route to Blair Atholl Mill could pass through Crieff, where there used to be a mill with an interesting breastshot paddle wheel. The A85 could then be taken to Perth, which you should not pass through without acknowledging its dependence on waterwheels for power. The city lade is believed to have been cut in the fifteenth century, since when it has supplied two 16ft diameter wheels at the Upper City Mill and a similar-sized wheel at the Lower City Mill. Perth Foundry was also, at one time, powered by a 14ft diameter undershot wheel. Near by, Stanley has been a centre for water-powered cotton mills which, because of Sir Richard Arkwright's influence, bear comparison with his mill at Belper in Derbyshire. At one time huge water-wheels provided 400hp, and in order to feed them tunnels had to be driven through the hill to reach the River Tay. Gilkes turbines have long since replaced the wheels.

Blair Atholl Mill is reached by taking the A9 through Pitlochry along the valley of the River Tummel to the point where the River Garry joins the River Tilt, which supplies the water to the mill. This was at one time a ruin, not having worked for fifty years, and a favourite place for children to hide when they were supposed to be at school. But John Ridley Projects Ltd, with the help of the Job Creation programme and a retired miller, Mr W. S. Sharp of Abernethy, have admirably restored the mill. It has some very interesting ancillary equipment, including a wire machine for grading flour, sieves for separating dust from the grain, and a rattler for removing lumps from oatmeal. Visitors can see the mill working, with an output of about 1cwt an hour, and can purchase stone-ground flour. There is a tea room, and the old mill stables are now a bakery producing bread, oatcakes, shortbread and scones, all with wholemeal flour.

72 Blair Atholl Mill, Pitlochry, Perth

On now to Balbirnie Mill near Brechin, which is part of the Southesk estate. The Bishops of Brechin probably built the first mill here in about 1500. Since then it has suffered several times from fire damage, particularly in 1917. In 1924 it had a Shanks single-cylinder diesel engine installed to supplement the wheel – the mill employed eight men at that time. The undershot wheel is 15ft in diameter, in cast iron with timber paddles, and is capable of producing between 25 and 30hp. At one time there were two kilns, but now there is only one. A craft shop and restaurant occupy part of the premises, but the sad fact at the moment of writing is that the owners cannot find a tenant to operate the mill, though it is open to public view.

Other mills to look for in the area include the grain and threshing mills in Arrat and the three mills in Glamis – one originally a lint mill and now a sawmill, one a corn mill and now a joiner's shop, and the other, Milton corn mill, still working when last heard of. Elsick Mill, at Fetteresso in Kincardine, had three external wheels and full machinery, which it is hoped have been at least retained, if not restored.

Take the A944 from Aberdeen to reach Montgarrie Mill near Tully-nessle; this is a meal mill with an iron overshot wheel 25ft in diameter and 4ft wide, with chain drive and gearbox. By following a route through Elgin, East Grange Mill at Kinloss near Forres can be reached. In 1976, Mr Grigor Butler witnessed the end of at least two centuries' milling here. However, he still uses the mill for grinding cattle feed. It could be used for threshing or for grinding simply by changing bevel pinions. The wheel, 13ft 6in in diameter and 4ft 4in wide, is of iron with larch buckets; it could develop at least 12hp and was capable of grinding 5½–6 bolls of meal per hour (a boll being 140lb).

Cantray Mill, an old corn mill with twin wheels and a kiln, can be reached by taking the B9006 off the main A96. Then take the A9 through Aviemore to Kingussie to the Highland Folk Museum, where a clack mill with horizontal wheel, taken from Back on the Isle of Lewis, has been reconstructed. A route round Loch Ness via the A86 and A82 can be taken as far as Milton; then the A833 leads on to the Old Milbrain Mill near Strathpeffer, where bed and breakfast accommodation is now provided. Nearby is the Millrain Mill near Fodderty, and further on Craig Mill, Rosskeen, which has been beautifully maintained by the miller.

The next call might be Gledfield Mill, one mile from Ardgay on the River Carron. This was built towards the end of the nineteenth century and worked until just after the last war. It is open to the public and an adjoining shop sells oatmeal, local produce and knitwear.

73 Remains of the mill at Durness, Sutherland

To make a circular tour of the north of Scotland, take the A836 and then the A838 as far as Durness on the north coast. Though the mill here is only a ruin near the ruins of a church and a group of cottages in a rather desolate spot, it is an interesting example of the simple type of building found with a horizontal mill. Continue along the A838 until it rejoins the A836, which passes through Forrs, where there is an overshot wheel. On now to John o'Groats; just to the south the mill at Canisbay has an overshot wheel and has worked recently.

Over in Orkney near Dounby is one of the most interesting of the simpler mills surviving in Britain, with a Norse horizontal wheel. Dry-stone walling supports a turf roof and the water flows right through the mill. The wheel is unusual, having its blades fixed at two levels. Winnowing is done by simply opening a 'wild door' to allow the chaff to be blown away. The mill has been renovated by the Orkney Archaeological Society and is in the care of the Department of the Environment. There is also the Tormiston Mill at Stennes in Orkney. Most of the equipment can be seen, but is not working at the moment. A craft shop and restaurant have been set up for visitors. One of the last working clack mills is the Troswick Mill at Dunrossness in Shet-

74 The two-hundred-year-old mill at Glendale, Isle of Skye

land. It grinds oats and some barley, and is driven by the Clumlie Burn. There is also a working model mill in Lerwick Museum. It has been reported that efforts are being made to restore an old mill on Fair Isle.

Return to the mainland and cross the country to the Isle of Skye, where a similar type of mill can be found. Glendale Mill is 200 years old, though its iron overshot wheel was installed in 1902, replacing a wooden one. For fifty-eight years it stood idle until it was restored in 1972 with the original machinery and peat-fired kiln.

Moving south on the mainland again, the old Corpach Mill in Kilmallie, near Fort William, has been converted for the use of a yacht club, but still has some mill machinery and an ice house for storing salmon. Following the A828 south will bring you to Bonawe, beside Loch Etive in Argyll. This is one of the most complete charcoal-smelting sites to survive. Iron ore was imported by sea from Cumberland, and a high-quality iron produced. The wheel pit can be clearly seen on a well restored and maintained site. Further south in Furnace, on the banks of Loch Fyne through Inveraray, is a similar site where a wheel operated bellows for the furnace and the tilt-hammers of the forge. It has yet to be restored as completely as the one at Bonawe.

Returning to the border country, the route may pass through areas like Paisley and Johnstone that have been rich enough in water power to support textile mills of no mean size. Now much of Scotland's water power goes into hydro-electric plants, as countless visitors to the 'Bonny Banks of Loch Lomond', for example, will have noticed.

WALES

The mountain streams and rivers of Wales have provided tremendous power in the past for a variety of purposes. Apart from the expected corn mills, much use of water power has been made for iron-smelting rolling mills, foundries and forges, tin-plate works, slate quarries, lead and copper mines and even gold mines. Many sites are now no more than overgrown ruins with evidence of a wheel pit or a mill race.

A tour of Welsh mills must include the Folk Museum in Cardiff. With this aim in mind, Skenfrith Mill in the Monnow Valley is an interesting point at which to begin. In a quiet spot, twelve miles from Abergavenny and eight miles from Monmouth, it has an external undershot wheel with open paddles. It is adjacent to Skenfrith Castle, which it probably served several hundred years ago.

From Skenfrith, take the road into Monmouth and then the Chepstow road to pass Llandogo. The site is much overgrown, but is important as the location of the early Coed Ithel blast furnace, where charcoal smelting began in the mid-seventeenth century. The wheel pit can be seen and the watercourse to the River Wye can be traced.

In the Welsh National Museum in Cardiff is a model and a fragment of the only known Roman gold mine in Britain – at Dolaucothi near Pumpsaint. The Romans constructed three aqueducts to bring water to the site. To the north-west of Cardiff is the St Fagans open-air museum, where the Esgair Moel Mill – one of the last water-powered fulling mills to be in production – was taken from its original site near Llanwrtyd, Breconshire, in 1953 and rebuilt to produce cloth for sale at the museum.

Taking the road across country to Pembrokeshire, there are several water-powered sites to be explored if you have the time. For example, at the Neath Abbey ironworks a wheel pit remains, along with other blast-furnace parts. But one of the most interesting mills in South Wales is the French tidal mill at Carew, north of Tenby. Fortunately, it has been restored and is open to the public. It has two undershot wheels each driving three pairs of stones. Originally the south wheel was intended for corn grinding and the north wheel for producing bone fertiliser. Tidal water is stored in a 23 acre pond which was formed by building a dam across the Carew estuary.

75 Skenfrith Mill on the River Monnow, Gwent

Only a few miles to the north, near Narberth, is Blackpool Mill, a large, impressive-looking building. The water flows through an arch under the roadway and under the building. It last worked commercially in the 1950s but was restored by the owner, Lady Dashwood, in 1968, and visitors to the craft shop and restaurant may view the machinery.

Through Haverfordwest – where the Castle Museum has some machinery from Llanwhaden Mill – and five miles north is the Nant-y-Coy Mill near Wolf's Castle. This is part of a wildlife conservation area and is privately owned. Its overshot wheel has not worked for over twenty-five years, but a visit is well worthwhile because of the museum and nature walk.

Travelling further north, you will reach the museum of the woollen industry at Drefach-Felindre near Newcastle Emlyn; this has a water-wheel and exhibits of water-powered machinery. In Newcastle Emlyn itself is the Felin Geri Mill, which received a European Architectural Heritage Year Award in 1975, following restoration. Originally it was a flour mill, but a second wheel was added to drive a circular saw. The mill now produces flour again, which is available in the mill shop.

A different use of an overshot wheel can be found at Y Felin Wlân (Rock Mills), a woollen mill at Capel Dewi, two miles past Llandysul, operated by John Morgan & Son. The mill was built in about 1890 and has its original wheel, which can still be seen, providing power for carding and spinning. The mill shop has a wide range of gifts and mill crafts for sale.

From Capel Dewi, the road reaches the coast at Aberaeron, north of New Quay. Here, until the 1940s, water-driven tilt-hammers had forged sickles, shovels and the like for nearly a hundred years. Ten miles from Aberystwyth is the old lead and silver mine at Llywernog. After being worked for around 150 years, it stood in ruins for about seventy years until restoration work began in 1973. Now a 7 acre site is being developed as an exhibition centre for the history of mineral mining in Wales. There are two particular features of interest: the wheel pit indicates that it had quite a large wheel, 55ft in diameter in fact, and its supply of water came along a leat over six miles long.

At Talybont, about seven miles north-east of Aberystwyth, there is a woollen mill, though originally the water power was used for smelting in local lead mines. The Lerry tweed mills are open for the public to see the hand and power looms in operation. Across country at Newtown is another woollen mill and craft shop where, as well as examining the external wheel, the visitor can see demonstrations of hand-weaving. A little further east, four miles from Montgomery, is Bacheldre Mill in Church Stoke. It has a long history and worked commercially until 1963. It has now been restored and is in full working order.

This area of Wales is rich in terms of both the variety and the extent of use that has been made of the waterwheel. In the Llanidloes area, on a tributary of the River Wye, is the Nant Iago lead mine, which used to have a 60ft diameter waterwheel. Its output varied but reached a peak of 176 tons of lead in one year. The Bryntail Mine on the River Clywedog used to grind barytes by millstones and is now a site in the care of the Department of the Environment.

A little further north, in a disused slate quarry at Llwyngwern near Machynlleth, is the Centre for Alternative Technology. The intentions of the organisers to demonstrate and investigate energy conservation appear admirable, but I have yet to see the waterwheel in action, despite several visits, or to appreciate its design. A narrow overshot wheel 10ft in diameter has been constructed, though its launder appears to be too short for the water to fall beyond the centre line of the wheel in an orthodox manner. It has a limited supply of water, taking the 120–140 gallons per minute exhaust water leaving a Pelton wheel, and so develops only about a quarter of a horsepower, turning at 6–7rpm.

Further north still, near Dolgellau, was a gold-recovery plant at the Bedd-y-Coedwr Mine, which used a waterwheel system known as Britten Pans. Many years ago it changed its name to the Princess

76 Where Welsh tweeds are woven by the power of a waterwheel at Talybont

Marina Mine and soldiered on until 1970. Now the Forestry Commission has removed the machinery and had it re-erected at the Maesgwm Centre, Ganllwyd. The Moelwyn Mills at Blaenau Ffestiniog have a set of fulling stocks which were probably the last in the country to work. The framework is of cast iron and transmission is by belt and gearing. The hammer heads and shafts are massive pieces of oak wedged into iron boxes.

Tempting as it may be to go on to the delightful Betws-y-Coed, turn back on the A496 and aim for Portmadoc. From there, take the A487 to Caernarvon; about six miles out of Portmadoc is Garn Dolbenmaen and a little further on, in Golan, the Brynkir woollen mill. Although this is now worked by water turbine, it still has the original overshot wheel and it is in working order.

Continue now on the road through Caernarvon and on to Anglesey. The journey across the island is well worthwhile because in Llanddeusant is Howell Mill. Mrs Williams, the proud owner of this working mill, is delighted to be able to write: 'I still have a miller, and ducks on the pond.' The mill has been in her late husband's family since 1740. When recent restoration work was completed, the architect entered the project in a competition run by the Royal Institute of Chartered Surveyors, *Country Life* and Times Newspapers. It won first award for its group and the mill continues to serve a wide agricultural community on the island.

Back on the mainland and travelling down the A5, there is a most important mill to see at Pentrefoelas, six miles beyond Betws-y-Coed. This mill is in full operation and run by the energetic Mrs Margaret Horsfield, who describes white flour and white sugar as 'the curse of civilisation'. A trained osteopath, herbalist and vegetarian, she is a great advocate of health foods and particularly wholewheat flour. Pentrefoelas Mill produces wholewheat flour, oatmeal, muesli and barley, rye and maize flour. In the old village school nearby, a bakery and shop have been set up and the range of breads, cakes, biscuits and other products is quite remarkable. From it, health food stores over a very wide area are supplied with their products. The mill is powered by a 30ft diameter overshot wheel of compass-arm construction which has metal spokes and rims and wooden buckets.

In Clywd there has been a prolific use of water power, so if you have time for a detour take the A543 to Holywell where the Greenfield Valley has powered a cotton mill, flour mills and a copper-smelting works. Little remains that is not overgrown of the latter, but the Holywell and Abbey mills still exist.

Further south, the Mold district has had several lead mines such as Owain Glyndwr, Gwern-y-Mynydd and Maeshafn; at the latter there is a pair of wheel pits side by side. The Cefn-y-Bedd wire mill in Ruabon has little left for the visitor to see except for part of the race and a cottage, but it is believed to have been connected with a similar mill in Wrexham. The Bersham blast furnace was an important site in its eighteenth-century heyday; it was built by Charles Lloyd, who did much to develop the iron industry in North Wales in the early eighteenth century. There are some remains among the farm buildings which now occupy the site. One cannot leave Wales without a look at the picturesque black and white mill in Rossett, just inside the border, with its external paddle wheel. The oak-framed building has the date 1661 carved on it.

The visit should have made it clear that the waterwheel has been of great value to Wales in the past, and that much remains to prove it.

GLOSSARY

Alarm Warning of low level of grain in the hopper

Ark Bin for grain or meal

Arms Spokes of a waterwheel

Aspirator Device for cleaning grain

Axle tree Wooden shaft on which a waterwheel is mounted

Backwatering Falling back of water in the tail race on to the wheel, with braking effect

Balance weights Lead weights set into top of runner stone to achieve balance

Balance box Patent method of fitting balance weights

Bedstone Fixed or bottom millstone

Bill *See* mill-bill

Bin Container for grain stored on the top or garner floor

Bist Small bag of bran to kneel on or to support the elbow during stone dressing

Bit Metal tool which fits into thrift for stone dressing

Blade *See* float

Blue stone Imported Continental millstone

Bolter Device for dressing flour

Bosom Depression round the edge of the eye of the runner stone

Brayer Beam of the hursting; part of tentering gear

Breast Central third of a millstone's radius

Breast or breastshot wheel Wheel which is struck by the water at or about axle level

Bridge tree Part of hursting supporting the bearing at the foot of the stone spindle

Bridging box Mounting for a thrust bearing for stone spindle or upright shaft

Brigging Process of ensuring that the stone spindle is vertical

Buckets Fittings around the wheel to hold water

Burr stone Millstone quarried near Paris

Centrifugal reel separator Device for dressing flour

Clasp-arm wheel Wheel with spokes forming a square around the shaft

Clewer Control hatch for water supply to wheel

Click Catch used to lock the winding gear of the penstock or the rack and pinion of other water controls

Clow or clough Sluice

Cogs Teeth of gear wheels

Cog pit or cog hole Part of ground floor containing pit wheel and engaging drive to stones

Compass-arm wheel Wheel whose spokes radiate from the shaft on which it is mounted

Composition stone Man-made stone consisting of carborundum and other abrasive materials

Cracking Process of cutting fine grooves or cracks on lands of the stones

Crook string String used to regulate opening from hopper to shoe

Crown wheel Large cog wheel at the top of the upright shaft to engage bevel gears for driving other machinery on stone floor

Crutch pole *See* quant

Damsel Device for jogging the shoe to regulate grain flow to stones

Dresser Device for grading flour

Dressing Process of sharpening millstones; also a refining process for flour

Drifting *See* furrowing

Elevator Equipment for lifting grain or meal

Eye Opening in runner stone through which grain passes; also term used for central part of a millstone when dressing

Face wheel Cog wheel with cogs on face or side of wheel instead of on its outer edge

Facing *See* staffing

False board Upper 'door' of hatch to undershot wheel

Felloe Section of the rim of a wheel

Flaunch or flanch Circular plate of metal on the hub or rim of a waterwheel to which arms are bolted

Flawing *See* staffing

Floating mill Wheel and millstones mounted on a boat

Floats Wood or metal blades or paddles of a waterwheel

Flood gate or flood hatch Sluice to divert water from wheel to overflow stream

Flop jack Device for lifting water

Flume Channel bringing water to the wheel

Footbrass Lining and wearing surface in a footstep bearing

Footstep bearing Thrust bearing in which gudgeon of upright shaft revolves

French stones *See* burr stones

Furrowing Process of cutting furrows in stone faces

Furrows Grooves cut into stone surfaces to produce sharp grinding edge

Gable Triangular frame, usually wooden, used to check that a stone is level

Garner Top floor of a mill where grain is stored

Gimbal Part of support for runner stone

Glut box Top bearing for quant in overdrift milling

Governor Regulator for controlling the amount of water flowing on to the wheel or for automatic tentering

Great spur wheel Large spur wheel mounted on upright shaft transmitting power to drive stones

Greek mill Early mill with horizontal wheel

Gripe-driven *See* overdrift

Grist Usually refers to animal feed ground at a mill

Grutte Bush in a bedstone of a Norse mill

Gudgeon Metal journal in the end of a wooden shaft

Hackle plate Cover plate over the spindle bearing in a bedstone

Hackle screws Adjusting screws used in remounting a runner stone

Handspikes Tools used in lifting a runner stone

Harp Sector of a stone's surface as divided for dressing; also, a template for marking out the face of a stone

Hatch Movable gate in sluice or penstock

Head race Stream of water above the mill wheel

Headsill *See* sill

Heft or helve Handle for holding stone-dressing tools

Hiddle Bundle of twigs or branches used to form a dam or embankment to hold back water

High breast wheel Waterwheel receiving water above axle height

High milling Process of milling, popular on the Continent, involving gradual reduction in several stages

Hopper Wooden box which receives grain from bin floor and passes it to the stone via the shoe

Horizontal wheel Wheel revolving in a horizontal plane on a vertical shaft

Horse Wooden framework supporting the hopper above the millstones

Hulling The removal of husks of cereals

Hunting cog Additional cog to avoid exact ratio, preventing same wear on each cog for every revolution

Hurst or hursting Timber or sometimes metal framework supporting millstones

Hurstle *See* tun

Hutch Corn bin in the loft

Jack ring Part of the mechanism for disengaging a stone nut

Kibbler Ancillary equipment for coarse-grinding beans and other foodstuffs

Lade *See* flume

Lands Flat parts of the grinding surfaces of millstones

Lantern wheel or lantern pinion Old type of gearing in wood

Launder Trough carrying water to a wheel

Lay shaft Shaft transmitting power to additional equipment such as a sack hoist

Leat *See* head race

Ligger *See* bedstone

Lightening tree Adjustable part of wooden framework in Norse mill

Low breast wheel Waterwheel receiving water below axle height

Low milling Method of milling in a single operation

Low-shottes Early form of weir to restrict level of water

Lucam Cabin jutting out from bin floor of mill, containing hoist gear

Mace head Method of supporting a runner stone

Many heights Stepped wedges used in lifting a runner stone

Meal spout Chute conveying meal from stones to sacks

Middlings Middle grade of flour when passed through a dresser

Mill-bill Carbon steel tool for stone dressing: handle and 'bit'

Miller's willow Twig used to form a return spring to shoe

Mill-eye Chute for flour as it leaves the skirting of the stones
Mill race *See* head race
Mill-rind *See* rynd
Mill-staff *See* paint-staff
Millstones Made of French burr, Derby Peak, composition, etc
Neck box Bearing in the centre of a bedstone
Nether stone *See* bedstone
Noria wheel Vertical wheel used for irrigation
Norse mill Mill with horizontal wheel common in northern Europe
Overdrift Method of driving millstones from above
Overshot wheel Type of wheel in which water falls over the top
Overtails Larger impurities removed from grain by sieving
Paddles *See* floats
Paint-staff Wooden straight-edge for testing the surface of a millstone
Peak stone Millstone quarried in the Peak District, mainly of Derbyshire
Penstock or pen trough Trough carrying water to a wheel
Pick Pointed metal 'bit' or tool for dressing
Pinion The smaller gear wheel of a pair
Pit wheel Gear wheel, parallel to waterwheel, inside the mill
Pitch-back wheel Type of wheel in which water falls into the buckets just before top centre
Plansifter Equipment for sieving flour
Poncelet wheel Type of undershot waterwheel developed by General Poncelet
Pond bay Dam or embankment of the pond
Poppet Frame supporting pulleys for ropes used in hoisting
Proof-staff Steel straight-edge for checking a paint-staff
Quant or quill Driving shaft in an overdriven mill
Race Channel of water to or from the wheel
Raddle A mixture of red-oxide and water applied to paint-staff to mark high spots on stone faces
Rap Hardwood block fixed on the shoe taking the rap of the damsel
Reducing The final stages in roller milling in which smooth rolls reduce the endosperm to white flour
Reel Silk-covered wooden cylinder of a bolter
Reel separator *See* separator
Rigger Band wheel; also a pulley driving belting
Rim gearing Use of a gear wheel taking direct drive from the rim of a water-wheel
Rungs Old term for floats or paddles
Runner stone Upper millstone
Rynd or rind Metal bridge across the eye of the runner stone
Sack hoist Method of lifting grain to garner floor
Scratching *See* cracking
Scribe Curved steel marker used in fitting new cogs
Separator Equipment for removing impurities from grain
Shelling First process in grinding oats in which the husks are removed
Shoe Chute from hopper to eye of runner stone

Shroud Outer casing at circumference of wheel to produce enclosed buckets
   or floats
Shuttle Sluice
Sickle dressing Method of stone dressing using curved furrows
Sile Type of rynd used in some Norse mills
Sill Top of wall to weir or dam
Skirt Outer edge of stone; also outer third of stone's surface when dressing
Skirting boards Wooden frame round bedstone
Slip cogs Removable cogs to allow a pinion to be taken out of gear
Smutter Machine for removing dirt and diseased particles from wheat
Sole plate Bottom board of bucket on waterwheel
Sole tree Bottom beam in framework supporting stones in Norse mills
Staffing Process for checking flatness of stone surfaces
Starter box Device used on a large wheel to set it in motion
Starts Wooden or metal post supports for the floats of a wheel
Stitching *See* cracking
Stone nut Pinion which engages with spur wheel and drives stone spindle
Stone spindle Shaft which supports and drives the runner stone
Tail race Stream below the wheel
Tentering Process of regulating space between stones for fineness of flour
Thone Wet or damp: term applied to stones, grain etc
Thrift Handle for mill-bill or pick
Throughs Good grain which passes through a sieve
Tide mill Mill using the force of water caused by the ebb and flow of the tide
Tilt-hammer Forge hammer operated by a cam shaft turned by a waterwheel
Tirl Impeller in a Norse mill
Tiver *See* raddle
Toebrass Part of the toe bearing in which a stone spindle revolves
Trammel Wooden gauge used to check the position of a runner stone and
   spindle
Trieur Device for removing impurities from grain
Trough Tank or channel of wood or metal carrying water to top of (overshot)
   wheel
Trundle wheel *See* lantern wheel
Tun Wooden casing around millstones
Underdrift Method of driving millstones from below
Undershot wheel Wheel driven by impulse of water passing underneath
Vane *See* float
Vat *See* tun
Wallower Small toothed wheel on upright shaft in gear with the pit wheel
Weir Dam across steam to divert water to the mill
Widdershins Method of dressing a stone – against the sun
Wire machine Method of dressing flour
Yoke and chain Method of disengaging a stone nut

BIBLIOGRAPHY

Early reference books
Agricola, G., *De Re Metallica* (Basle, 1556; translated H. C. and L. M. Hoover, Constable, 1950)
Bennett, R., and Elton, J., *The History of Corn-Milling* (4 vols, Simpkin Marshall, 1899; vol II, *Watermills and Windmills*, republished E. P. Publishing Ltd, 1973)
Fairbairn, Sir W., *A Treatise on Mills and Millwork* (2 vols, Longmans Green, London, 1878)
Fitzherbert, Sir A., *Boke of Surveyinge and Improvements* (1539)
Glynn, J., *On the Power of Water to turn Mills* (Weale, London, 1853)
Gray, A., *The Experienced Millwright* (1806)
Stow, J., *Survey of London* (1558; republished W. J. Thomas, 1842)
Sutcliffe, J., 'Instructions for Designing and Building a Corn Mill', from *A Treatise on Canals and Reservoirs* (1816)

Publications of the Wind and Watermill Section of the Society for the Protection of Ancient Buildings
Lord Wilson of High Wray, *Watermills – An Introduction* (1956, revised 1973)
Wailes, Rex, *Tide Mills*, parts I and II (1956)
Gardner, E. M., *Tide Mills*, part III (*The Three Mills, Bromley-by-Bow*) (1956)
Pelham, Dr R. A., *Fulling Mills* (1956)
Reid, K. C., *Watermills and the Landscape* (1959)
Wilson, Paul N., *Watermills with Horizontal Wheels* (1960)
Luckhurst, D., *Monastic Watermills*
Shorter, Dr A. H., *Water Paper Mills* (1966)
Rollins, J. G., *Needle Mills* (1970)

Transactions of the Newcomen Society
'Savery's invention of floating mills', vol III
'Watermills in Devon and Cornwall', vol IV
'Tidal mill at Revere Beach, U.S.A.', vol VI
'Watermills in Kent', vol VII
'Watermills in Lancashire', vol VII
'Early English mills', vol VII
'Lead mining in West Yorks', vol VII
'Watermills', vol VIII

'Early millstones for milling corn', vol IX
'Watermills in England', vol IX
'Flour milling', vol X
'Watermills', vol X
'Watermills in England and Germany', vol XI
'Waterwheels for mine pumping', vol XII
'Shetland mills', vol XIII
'Shetland mills and wheels', vol XIV
'Watermill at Long Island', vol XV
'Telford on watermills'
'Mills in the pottery industry', vol XVII
'Water power in Westmorland', vol XVIII
'Hammer mills in Cornwall', vol XVIII
'Hammer mills at Middleburg', extra paper no 4
'Tide mills in England and Wales', vol XIX
'Old water wheel at Seacroft, Leeds', vol XIX
'Millstones in wind and water mills', vol XXIV
'Some notes on Dutch watermills', vol XXVII
'Water power as the foundation of Sheffield's industries', vol XXVII
'Smeaton's Enquiry concerning the Natural Power of Water and Wind', vol XXX
'Observations on the history of water power', vol XXX
'Dorset watermills', vols XXXV and XXXVI
'Gunpowder mills of Westmorland and Furness', vol XXXVI
'Broadstone Mill, Corvedale', vol XXXVI
'Peak millstones and Hallamshire grindstones', vol XXXVI
'Suffolk watermills', vol XXXVII
'Water power in the north of Ireland', vol XXXIX
'Water-driven mills for grinding stone', vol XXXIX
'Dorset watermills' (addendum), vol XLI

Local studies
Adorian, P., *The Story of Gibbons Mill* (Wind and Watermill Section, Society for the Protection of Ancient Buildings, 1970)
Allison, K. J., *East Riding Watermills* (East Yorkshire Local History Society, 1975)
Ashton, N., *Watermills in Leicestershire* (1977)
Austin, W., *Domesday Mills of Bedfordshire* (Bedfordshire Historical Records Society, 1916)
Berkley, Mrs, 'Old Worcestershire Watermills', *Transactions of Worcestershire Archaeological Society*, vol 2 (1935)
Booth, D. T. N., *Warwickshire Watermills* (Midland Wind and Watermills Group, 1978)
Bunn, R. F. I., 'The Manorial Mills of Manchester', *Mem Proc Manchester Literary and Philosophical Society* (1949)
Clough, R. T., *Some North Country Watermills* (RIBA, 1954)

Copeland, R., *Cheddleton Flint Mill and the History of Pottery Milling 1726–1900* (Cheddleton Flint Mill Preservation Trust, 1969)

Craddock, R., 'Mills and Milling', *Lincolnshire Industrial Archaeology* (1969)

Ellis, C. M., 'A gazetteer of water, wind and tide mills of Hampshire', *Proceedings of the Hampshire Field Club*, vol 25 (1968)

Foreman, W., *Watermills of Oxford* (measured drawings)

Fraser, W., 'Some Derbyshire watermills', *Derbyshire Countryside* (Jan-Mar 1951)

Hillier, J., *Old Surrey Watermills* (1951)

Hoffman, S., 'The Passing of Birdham Mill', *Sussex County Magazine* (1937)

Major, J. K., *Woodbridge Tidemill* (1961)

——*Berkshire Watermills* (1964)

——*Mills of the Isle of Wight* (1969)

Messent, C. J. W., *Old Watermills of Norfolk* (1939)

Norris, J. H., 'Water-powered corn mills of Cheshire', *Lancashire and Cheshire Antiquarian Society* (1969)

Pelham, R. A., *The Old Mills of Southampton* (1963)

Percival, A., *Faversham's Gunpowder Industry* (The Faversham Society, 1967)

Prentis, W. H., *The Snuff-mill Story* (1970)

Rahtz, P., and Sheridan, K., 'Saxon watermill in Tamworth', *Transactions of South Staffordshire Archaeological and Historical Society* (1972)

Somervell, J., *Waterpower Mills of South Westmorland* (1930)

Tann, J., *Gloucestershire Woollen Mills* (David & Charles, 1967)

Wantage Industrial Archaeology Group, *Mills of the Ock* (1978)

Weaver, M. A., *The Tide Mill, Woodbridge* (Friends of Woodbridge Tide Mill, 1977)

Willoughby, R. W., 'Watermills in West Wiltshire', *Wiltshire Archaeological and Natural History Magazine* (1969)

Books on watermills and allied subjects

Davies-Shiel, M., *Watermills of Cumbria* (The Dalesman, 1979)

Finch, W. C., *Windmills and Watermills* (1933)

Freese, S. W., *Windmills and Millwrighting* (1957; reprinted David & Charles, 1971)

Hopkins, R. T., *Old English Mills and Inns* (1927)

Jespersen, A., *The Lady Isabella Waterwheel of Great Laxey* (published by the author, Virum, Denmark, 1954)

Long, G., *The Mills of Man* (1931)

Reynolds, J., *Windmills and Watermills* (Hugh Evelyn, 1970)

Skilton, C. P., *British Windmills and Watermills* (Collins, 1948)

Storck, J., and Teague, W. D., *Flour for Man's Bread* (Minneapolis, 1952)

Syson, L., *British Watermills* (Batsford, 1965)

Vialls, C., *Windmills and Watermills* (A & C Black, 1970)

Vince, J. T., *Discovering Watermills* (Shire Publications, 1970)

Wailes, Rex, *The English Windmill* (Routledge & Kegan Paul, 1954)

Walton, J., *Water-mills, Windmills and Horse-mills of South Africa* (C. Struik, 1974)

Industrial archaeology and other subjects
Ashmore, O., *The Industrial Archaeology of Lancashire* (David & Charles, 1969)
Buchanan, A., and Cossons, N., *The Industrial Archaeology of the Bristol Region* (David & Charles, 1969)
Butt, J., *The Industrial Archaeology of Scotland* (David & Charles, 1967)
Harris, H., *The Industrial Archaeology of the Peak District* (David & Charles, 1971)
Hudson, K., *The Industrial Archaeology of Southern England* (David & Charles, 1968)
Johnson, W. B., *The Industrial Archaeology of Hertfordshire* (David & Charles, 1970)
Marshall, J. D., and Davies-Shiel, M., *The Industrial Archaeology of the Lake Counties* (David & Charles, 1969)
Nixon, F., *The Industrial Archaeology of Derbyshire* (David & Charles, 1969)
Smith, D. M., *The Industrial Archaeology of the East Midlands* (David & Charles, 1965)
Todd, A. C., and Laws, P. G., *The Industrial Archaeology of Cornwall* (David & Charles, 1972)
Darby, H. C., *The Domesday Geography of Eastern England* (Cambridge University Press, 1952)
——and Cambell, E. M. J., *The Domesday Geography of South East England* (CUP, 1962)
——and Maxwell, I. S., *The Domesday Geography of Northern England* (CUP, 1962)
——and Terrett, I. B., *The Domesday Geography of Midland England* (CUP, 1954)
Gimpel, J., *The Medieval Machine* (Gollancz, 1977)

ACKNOWLEDGEMENTS

It must be acknowledged that many people have contributed to the compiling of material for this book. I am grateful to the many millers and mill owners who have welcomed me when I have visited them. Chatting to them has always been an enjoyable and interesting experience. Many others have corresponded with me, and their help has been equally valuable. I would also like to thank Mr Rex Wailes, who used his wealth of experience of mills to correct some of my earlier mistakes, and Mr Hallam Ashley, who provided many of the photographs. Mr Ashley's readiness to add interesting information about his visits to mills has been particularly appreciated. The staffs of a number of record offices have also been very helpful; local libraries have been the source of further information. Many friends and colleagues at Sandbach have been very willing to pass on information and have provided help in many ways. To my wife Jean and my two sons David and Michael, I am most grateful for their willingness to be taken on mill-searching journeys, for permitting so much inconvenience while the records were being compiled, and, in David's case, for help with some of the drawings.

Photographs are reproduced by permission of the following:

Dorothy Ashley: 56
Hallam Ashley: 9, 15, 16, 18, 19, 21, 23, 24, 25, 31, 32, 36, 37, 38, 39, 40, 41, 42, 43, 45, 46, 47, 48, 49, 54, 55, 69, 70, 73, 75
Author: 6, 10, 11, 12, 13, 17, 20, 44, 50, 52, 53, 58, 61, 65, 66
J. Allan Cash: 28, 33, 34, 35, 67
Cheshire Library and Museum Service: 63
Cowper & Co, Perth: 72
Cumbria County Planning Department: 68
Department of the Environment. Crown Copyright: 57
Mill owners: 22, 27, 51, 59, 60, 74
North-West Water Authority: 64
J. S. Peck, Truro: 29
Science Museum, London. Crown Copyright: 1, 2, 3, 4, 5, 7, 8, 14
John Topham Picture Library: 26, 62, 71, 76
West Air Photographs, Weston-super-Mare: 30

INDEX